Light in the Heart of Darkness

The Surprising Truth About Depression &
How to Free Yourself Completely From its Grips

Kevin Billett
Brandon Bays

Published by Best Seller Publishing®, Pasadena, CA
Best Seller Publishing® is a registered trademark
Printed in the United States of America.
ISBN: 978-1-946978-96-7

This publication is designed to provide accurate and authoritative information with regard to the subject matter covered. It is sold with the understanding that the publisher is not engaged in rendering legal, accounting, or other professional advice. If legal advice or other expert assistance is required, the services of a competent professional should be sought. The opinions expressed by the authors in this book are not endorsed by Best Seller Publishing® and are the sole responsibility of the author rendering the opinion.

Most Best Seller Publishing® titles are available at special quantity discounts for bulk purchases for sales promotions, premiums, fundraising, and educational use. Special versions or book excerpts can also be created to fit specific needs.

For more information, please write:
Best Seller Publishing®
1346 Walnut Street, #205
Pasadena, CA 91106
or call 1(626) 765 9750
Toll Free: 1(844) 850-3500
Visit us online at: www.BestSellerPublishing.org

Dedication

For My Father
William John Billett
A true example of the life-affirming power of
big-hearted love, positivity and vision

So the darkness shall be the light
And the stillness the dancing

T S Eliot

Table of Contents

Disclaimer

This is not a textbook on depression: it is not intended to be a comprehensive description of, or guide to, the condition. It is a practical book written to guide you out of depression, no matter who you are, where you are from or what your circumstances. It is a book written from the direct experience of liberation from depression, of uncovering its deepest root causes and resolving them completely. It is a book full of examples and stories that will, I trust, strike a chord of recognition - of 'me too' - somewhere deep inside you. You may wish to enquire as you read, 'What is my version of this circumstance or story?' and, 'How have my life experiences been similar?'

This book is not intended in any way to diagnose or treat any type of disease or illness. For such diagnosis and treatment please consult a qualified medical practitioner. The legal small print, which our lawyers insist on, is below:

Nothing contained in this publication is intended to represent, suggest, hold out or purport to claim whether expressly or by implication and in any context or on any interpretation that 'The Journey'® or any accredited practitioner or other representative of 'The Journey' or any services, work, processes, materials or products provided or presented by any accredited practitioner or any representative of 'The Journey' involve, comprise, offer or provide anything other than a process of guided introspection and self-discovery for individuals, or any kind of holistic or mystical or other cure for any physical, mental, psychological, psychiatric or other medical ailment, illness, condition, state or complaint, or that 'The Journey' or any such services, work, processes, materials or products are, might or could in any circumstances be or become a substitute, replacement for or alternative to specialized medical treatment and/or appropriate medical advice from properly qualified, trained and experienced practitioners.

What to Expect From This Book

Depression is considered the biggest 'psychological' disorder in the western world. If you are in the grip of depression you are not alone. Over 360 million people worldwide experience depression in some form or other.

We'll be alongside you as we explore what depression really is and how to up-root it from our lives. Along the way you'll be able to read, and experience, parts of Kevin's journey from the deepest depression to a new and fulfilled life.

We'll bust some myths about depression in Chapter 2 and look at our emotions and how we manipulate them in chapters 3 and 4, along the way discovering what depression really is and what really causes it. In Chapter 5 we'll learn how our beliefs shape our personal 'stories' and our perceptions of life, and in Chapter 7 we'll focus on some negative forces that contribute to depression and its intensity.

If that all sounds - well, depressing - then remember; this book, and the process work within it, gives you the opportunity to transform your life and be freed from depression forever.

Activities to help you understand the causes of depression, and ultimately free yourself from it, are on offer throughout this book. All we ask is that you commit to doing the work that is needed. Thousands of people like us have already done it, and you can too.

In Chapter 3 we'll look at how our decision making is driven by emotions. And in Chapter 4 you'll get to grips with the strategies or habits that you use to avoid or manipulate your emotions. In Chapter 5 you'll start to change your beliefs and release some of the related fears, and in Chapter 6 you'll discover a potent secret alternative to wrestling with your unwanted emotions.

Access to the directly transformational material, the guided introspections that will help you free yourself from depression, is in Chapter 9.

All of this healing process work is also available free online as audio downloads at www://kevinbillett.org/book-bonus/.

In chapter 10 you'll be making some decisions about staying healthy and positive, and making some supportive lifestyle choices. And in Chapter 11 we'll explore life's purpose and help you to discover yours.

Come with us on this journey - it will be worth it. The result of your willingness and honest inquiry will be a life richer than you ever imagined, and free from depression forever.

Before we finish our travels through the book we'll give you some pointers for where and how you could continue your journey, and offer you ideas for more things to read if you'd like to. Our websites www.thejourney.com and www.kevinbillett.org gives more ideas and opportunities too, so we hope you'll find some useful resources for sustaining you as you move forward, free from depression.

Kevin & Brandon

Foreword by Brandon Bays

Dear Reader,

When The Journey began some 24 years ago, I had a passionate prayer that has lived through me every day since: that this powerfully life transforming work find its way into the hands of those who truly seek to heal their lives and set themselves free.

I wanted people to have profoundly effective tools and healing process work that would set them free to live their lives fully, as a true expression of their authentic selves.

When I first began offering The Journey around the world, I became aware that of all life areas this method is successful in healing - emotional, physical, spiritual and mental - depression is the one area where we get the most consistently effective and lasting results, and the most exuberant feedback.

Depression has deeply impacted my own life so I have a deep personal wish to reach out to those who have suffered from depression or who currently grapple with it.

My father lived with medically diagnosed manic depression (bipolar disorder) for as long as I knew him. He was my hero, an extraordinary man, but he battled with depression for as long as I can remember and until the day he died.

Dad was an extreme perfectionist. As an engineering scientist during the Cold War era, he designed intercontinental missile detecting radar systems to protect the USA from the threat of potential Soviet attack. The immense pressure he felt from his job regularly overwhelmed him.

I returned home one weekend shortly after I had started my first semester at university. Dad was clearly in deep despair again, weighed down and crushed by the unbearable responsibility he was carrying.

He was completing his latest radar design and working long into the night; obsessively combing through every calculation, every digit, and every letter in his vast computer printouts, terrified that if he had made one mistake, made one miscalculation, millions of people might die as a result.

Wishing I could alleviate some of his pain - reach out to him to offer some tiny modicum of relief - I rose early one morning and wrote what I thought was a loving, caring note. I wrote that I was aware of the pressure he was under, how it was crushing him and that I wished somehow that he could trust in God to take some of the weight off his shoulders: that he could 'give his burden up to God' and trust that he would be supported. I wanted him to know he was not alone.

Mid-morning my Dad came out of his study; he looked anguished, desperate. Holding my note, hands shaking, he asked, "What do you mean 'give my burden up to God?'"

I looked into his eyes, not knowing how to answer. "Daddy, I just wish that somehow you could trust in God, that you could know you are supported, that you are not alone in this."

"But what do you mean, 'give my burden up to God?'"

"I don't know how to describe it Daddy." He gave me a look of helpless excruciating agony, then shook his head and went back into his study.

At noon I took the bus back to university with a knot in my gut and an inexplicable feeling of impending doom that I couldn't shake. When I got to in my dorm room the phone rang. My brother Chris' voice sounded strange. He said "Brandon, sit down."

"Chris, don't be so dramatic!" I replied, "What is it?"

"SIT DOWN!" he yelled. Then quietly, as if devoid of any emotion, he said "After you left, Daddy took his perfectly designed radar and delivered it to his desk at work. He came home, went into the garage, found some rope and hanged himself... He was still swaying when Linda found him."

I sat there stunned. I was mute, unable to breathe. And the picture of my note and the words 'give your burden up to God' flooded back to me. In that tiny instant I realized that Daddy had mistaken my meaning. He'd literally 'given his burden up to God', by taking his own life. I'd killed my Dad.

In that moment it was as if steel walls closed in around me. I became numb, frozen, incapable of feeling anything. No tears, no despair, no grief, no mourning, just an overwhelming coat of dull numbness I couldn't escape. It was as if someone had thrown away the key to my life.

And from that cataclysmic moment I lived for the next seven years frozen, covered in a relentless weight of something I did not have a name for that would not let up. No light could penetrate the haze of dullness I was in. I could feel no happiness, I had no sense of humor. If someone had asked I would not have said I was depressed. I wouldn't have known how to describe my condition except to say that it was pervasive, emotionless, devoid of any real juice or any genuine joy.

During that whole period I finished university, got married, went to graduate university and moved to New York City, but it all seemed to be happening as if from a distance. Like I was living someone else's life, disassociated and simply going through the motions. No matter how hard I tried, I just felt numb. The emotional distance from my true self, the overwhelming inability to shake myself free from this fog of what I now recognize was depression, pervaded my life.

Seven years after this initial shut down I found myself at a spiritual summer camp in western New York State. By now I was certified in many areas and disciplines of complementary medicine and personal growth and was firmly on my own spiritual path. I was what in spiritual circles is commonly called a 'seeker.' I think, in part at least, I was driven by a desire to find my way back home to myself, to the real me: to be able to feel again, to experience the natural highs and lows of living as an alive human being again. But I didn't know where to go to find it. It was buried too deep inside me to reach.

So, I immersed myself in the healing field, striving to be whole again, and my quest eventually brought me to this summer camp. There were all kinds of disciplines: meditation, yoga, herbology, nutrition, detox cleanses, spiritualism, Native American Indian wisdom complete with sweat lodges… on and on.

One evening after a sacred sweat lodge ceremony I came back to the little cottage I'd rented. A stranger knocked on the door and asked if my name was Brandon. He wanted to come in and have a conversation with me. I was from New York and naturally suspicious of strangers, even those at the same spiritual camp, so I politely refused him. He replied, "Did your father hang himself?"

That sure got my attention.

I invited him in and offered him tea. He shared that he was a spiritualist and that he'd 'received a message' from my Dad. He said, "Your Dad wants you to know it's not your fault and that he is at peace."

When he said the words "it's not your fault" it was like someone took a big chisel and hammered it into the heavy block of ice that I had become, and a crack rent straight through my being from top to bottom. It crashed through all my defenses and splayed me wide open emotionally. I thanked him, stunned at the news he had brought.

After he left the frozen ice began to melt. All the unshed tears I'd never been able to release, the anguish that I hadn't had access to, the loss I had no way of expressing-it all came pouring out as I sobbed and sobbed, releasing the seven years of pain that had been buried and hidden.

After three days, when it seemed that not one more tear could be wrung out of me, I was left at peace. It seemed that life had spontaneously graced me with the ability to release all that pent up pain and had at the same time given me the ability to finally forgive myself for something that had previously seemed unfor-givable. Suddenly I was able to feel again, in touch with the myriad emotions that are part of the glorious spectrum of our human existence. I felt free.

Rolling the cameras forward to the present, if you asked me, 'Have you ever experienced depression in your life?' I would unequivocally answer, "No, I am not the depressive type. I have a naturally sunny disposition." Yet looking back, I now realize that I spent seven years of my life in a trauma-induced depres-sion, unable to feel, ghost-walking through life. And when life decided to crash through my hardened shell, all my buried pain could finally emerge, be fully felt, expressed, and released. Most importantly, I was finally able to forgive myself. It was through this liberating experience that I was able to feel the juice of life again, to be myself again, to feel myself again.

Years later, when The Journey was born through my own direct experience of healing from a large tumor, I became aware that I had found a method for all of us to clear and heal our lives; to get to the emotional root causes of what had put our shutdowns in place and clear them out completely. When you do this, your strategies of shut down dissolve and disappear naturally. And, vitally, when we come to full self-forgiveness and forgiveness of life, it is as if we are given permission to live more freely, more openly, more honestly. We feel free to be ourselves, to live life from the full spectrum of what is possible for humans to experience. It opens the door for us to feel our own natural life force, to again experience the beauty and juice of life.

So, though I must admit I was unable to save my Dad or even to help myself out of the seven years of depression, I absolutely know now that with The Journey you have access to all the tools, the understanding, the profoundly effective process work that you need to completely free yourself to live life fully again, to feel alive and purposeful again.

And that is what excites me so much about this book. In your hands you are holding your key to freedom from depression; if you are willing to undergo the deeply healing process work offered.

When I started presenting The Journey Intensive in 1994, Kevin Billett (now my beloved life partner and main author of this book) arrived having been medically diagnosed with 'chemical' depression that was supposedly genetically inherited. He was on a cocktail of prescribed drugs that he felt were controlling his every waking moment. Through The Journey, he completely and utterly freed himself from depression and felt so grateful to life for his newfound freedom, for his ability to feel the colorful palette of all natural emotions, that he made it his life's mission to help others who suffer from shutdown and depression free themselves and find natural fulfillment in their own lives.

In this book you will join Kevin on his healing journey as he liberates himself from a chronic cyclical depression he lived with since childhood; a condition he was told he probably would never be free from. Then step-by-step, using Journeywork, and the tools we have jointly developed over the last two-plus decades, you will go through your own journey to freedom from the depression you may have experienced in your life.

Kevin dedicates his life to serving others in their healing and awakening. Take a look below (Fig. 1) at some before and after results achieved with a group that attended Kevin's workshop - Out of the Blue - in Melbourne Australia. Attendees were asked to fill in a questionnaire about their experiences of depression, stress and anxiety before the workshop and one month after it. As you can see the results are exciting!

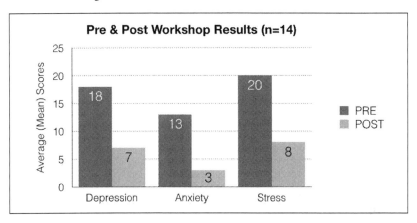

Figure 1: Average (mean) scores for levels of depression, anxiety & stress for the 14 matched pairs. N.B. These results are for those who completed both the pre and post survey.

Dr. Jill Beattie, who organized and supervised the research, made the comment below. (The graph above is taken directly from her report.)

"Four weeks after the completion of the 2½-day Out of the Blue workshop conducted in Australia February 2014, there was a significant decrease in depression, anxiety and stress scores, indicating an improvement in symptoms related to depression, anxiety and stress of the participants". Dr. Jill Beattie, Adjunct Senior Research Fellow, Monash University, Victoria, Australia

In this book Kevin offers the same teaching and uses the same techniques used in that workshop in Australia. And as a part of this book, free online, he will expertly guide you through a series of liberating audio processes and introspections that will allow you to gently, yet finally, become free from any mild to moderate depression that has shown up in your life. And if you're willing to actually give it a go, and **do the work** (not just passively read about it), you have the opportunity of fully liberating your life in every area.

So it's time to roll up your sleeves and let your journey to freedom begin. You have a whole new life of fulfillment and joy ahead of you!

In all Love,
Brandon

The Invitation

By the time I finally admitted the truth - that I was suffering from depression - it seemed too late. The pattern had a deeply ingrained hold on me, and it felt impossible that I would ever truly be free from it. I thought I would never again feel genuinely, unabashedly happy.

I had no belief at the time I first experienced Brandon's work, the Journeywork that forms the basis of this book, that it would set me free - but it did. It freed me from an almost lifelong cyclical experience of depression; it freed me from the habitual feelings of heaviness, pointlessness and overwhelm that I had carried for decades; and much more than this, it allowed me the enormous freedom of knowing the truth of my deepest, most essential self. It allowed me to find true and lasting light not at the end of a tunnel, not in some mythical Nirvana, but right there in the heart of the darkness.

My life has been completely and absolutely transformed during the 24 years since that time, and I have continued to regularly use and share with others the extraordinary insights and techniques that made this happen.

The fact that you are reading this book probably means you have some experience with depression, either directly and personally or indirectly, by witnessing others struggle. You know about its insidious force, its ability to sabotage and steal energy and willpower. You know of its downward spiral, its hopelessness and its darkness. You possibly know that there are many books available that teach us methods to be more positive, to cheer up and feel (at least temporarily) better, or the others that teach us how to manage, control and live with depression by making lifestyle changes, through changing diet or by taking medication.

This is not one of those books. Neither is this a textbook on depression, it is not a comprehensive guide to the condition.

This is a book about emotional freedom; it is aimed squarely at giving you the resources to find complete and lasting freedom from depression. It is based not on theories or wishful thinking, but on the direct personal experience of having suffered from depression, being totally freed from it and spending more than two decades using Journeywork to help others free themselves.

In this book we will look at what depression is and what it is not, what affects it both negatively and positively. And most important you will learn how to uncover the real causes of your own painful experience of life, and what to do to fully resolve and heal from the underlying causes of depression.

Your own life experiences will undoubtedly be different to mine, so as you read just stay open to a background awareness of your own examples, your own history, and know that the work here will eventually be deeply personal and pertinent to you. If old memories arise just be softly aware of them, and allow them to be present. They may eventually show up when you undergo some of The Journey introspections and clearing work.

I can't promise that it will be a comfortable ride, at times it may well be a deeply or sharply emotional experience. But what I know from long experience is that if you are willing to be truthful with yourself, if you are willing to let the teachings and revelations sink in and resonate inside you, so you can notice how you feel emotionally as you read, you will be able to genuinely explore and engage with the exercises and the work that is included here. The possibility exists that, like many thousands of people around the globe who have already experienced this work, you can find inner peace, you can be free.

If you bought this book for yourself, then it is clear that you are interested in the subject and in exploring some new approaches to clearing the pattern of depression. All I can ask is that you follow through with the reading and in particular that you give the process work, the guided introspections included here, a good go. This will give you the maximum chance of truly transforming your everyday experience of life.

If someone else bought you this book and suggested that you 'need' it, should read it, or might be helped by it, then you have a choice: you can continue to live life the way you are currently living it, sticking with what you already know, what you already do or don't do, feeling the way you currently feel; or you could choose to explore something fresh, something different that gives you at least the chance of making valuable and lasting shifts in your life. No one can ever force you to make changes that you do not want to make or are not yet ready to make, so truly the choice is yours. And if your life is not 100% the way you feel it should be, just be honest with yourself and ask, 'What have I got to lose by reading on with an open mind, and giving this a go?'

You do not have to have recognizable or diagnosed depression for the work here to help you. Some of us, like I did when I was younger, ignore the signs of depression we experience. Some of us even dismiss clinical diagnosis and pretend that nothing is wrong when something definitely is amiss. If you are in doubt, just read the section in Chapter 2 on symptoms of depression and check out if any of the listed symptoms feel familiar - though this is not by any means a comprehensive list, and though it is not a method for diagnosing depression, you may find it clarifying.

And most of us have ongoing issues, unresolved pains and traumas, in our lives. Journeywork can and does help with an enormous number of life issues, from feeling stressed, anxious or pressured by life, to feeling lost or listless, aimless, unsatisfied, or simply a bit 'blue'. So, whether or not you suffer from clinically diagnosed depression, there might be something transformational for you here in this book.

Ultimately, this book is an invitation to step into the real you, the authentic, whole, fulfilled self that already exists deep inside. This is an invitation into absolute freedom. It is your invitation to come home to your true self, and to live the life you were really meant to live. And, whatever your circumstance, the choice to accept this invitation is yours and yours alone.

To smooth your path, and help you to focus on your deeper inner experience while reading the book, I've avoided using reference marks or links to additional resources at any point. Instead, I've listed some recommended reading at the back of the book if you want to learn more about some of the subjects included here. The only links you will find in the text are ones that allow you to directly access what you need to get the highest and best results with this book and its work. Where I invite you to do an online exercise (called an introspection or a process) you'll see an icon like this:

One last point: there are almost always exceptions to every rule, and there are few ultimate truths. If you try hard enough you can always find a way to take a contrarian stance, to naysay any premise, and I recognize in my own character the tendency to do this. So what I have found invaluable over the years, when presented with some new or challenging information, is to change my old habitual question, "Is this absolutely true?" into the new question, "Is this useful or potentially beneficial?" I find this more flexible approach gets me out of my pre-existing mental 'box' and allows me to think more laterally, more creatively. It leads to greater and deeper personal insights, and eventually to more resolution and fulfillment.

So when reading through some of the more testing assertions laid out here, you might like to take a similar stance. If you find some of the information uncomfortable or confrontational, rather than mismatching or judging the statement, simply ask, "Does this viewpoint have potential value?" or "If I explored this perspective openly, might it help me?"

Brandon and I trust that as you Journey with us you will discover deep inside yourself the limitless freedom that is the cradle, the essence and the theme of our own lives. We pray that you find the blazing light that exists in the core, the heart, of all darkness.

Bon voyage!
Kevin

CHAPTER 1

An All Too Familiar Feeling

In the summer of 1994 I thought my depression had reached its nadir; that it could get no worse, no more painful. The combination of bereavement, business failure, job loss, marital separation, impending divorce and loss of my home had so overloaded my coping mechanisms, had so compounded the effects of my normally cyclical depression, that I felt as if I had been drawn helplessly down into a whirlpool of darkness.

The effects of the cocktail of anti-depressive drugs I had been prescribed, at least in the short term, made things even worse. I was warned of possible side effects, but had no clue how painful they would be.

For the first two months after starting the medication it felt as if I had taken the lid off a Pandora's Box of chaotic negativity and climbed inside. My body shook, I was in constant physical pain and I slept an average of 90 minutes in total each day, even with the sleeping pills I was taking. I lay for hours and hours, day and night, with my eyes closed and my mind spinning on a nightmare rollercoaster ride. I could barely walk, and could barely eat. I tried to figure out how I could and would commit suicide to make the pain stop, but couldn't find the focus or the wherewithal to make a realistic plan.

Then, gradually, the most severe side effects began to subside and I was left in a new and semi-surreal existence. The pain and the sleeplessness lessened, then disappeared, but I felt as if I was strangely supplanted into someone else's body, someone else's life. I became rude and aggressive, edgy and spiteful, towards everyone, from my best friends to people I did not even know. I began to party hard and drink more alcohol than even I was used to. I felt frantically out of control but couldn't care less. I did not recognize myself.

I'd lived with depression for most of my life, but this was the worst it had ever been. The help I'd sought from medicine and psychotherapy in some ways made things worse. I'd tried personal development, affirmations, positive thinking, meditation and reading spiritual texts - pretty much anything and everything I could find or that well-meaning friends told me about. I'd listen to audio tapes or go to weekend seminars and feel good for a while, only to slide back into the same depressive darkness.

Now I know that my struggle with depression is all too common and is experienced in some form or other by some 360 million people worldwide. Depression is considered the biggest 'psychological' disorder in the western world. There are predictions by the World Health Organization (WHO) that by 2020 depression will be the second-biggest cause of disability in the world. Only heart disease will outpace its corrosive effects.

In the United States of America, it is estimated that 35 to 40 million people will experience depression at some point in their lives. Today one in every ten people takes some kind of antidepressant medication. In women between ages 40 and 50, the figure is one in four. In 2013 there were more than 1.4 million Americans receiving federal disability funds for 'mood disorders' - meaning that they could not work due to depression and other such problems. In the United Kingdom in 2014-15 17.3% of the population - more than 11 million people - were estimated to show 'Some signs of depression or anxiety'.

EurActiv Germany reports that in Germany there was a 70 per cent increase in depression between the years 2000 and 2013, and that in the European Union as a whole some 30 million people suffer from depression. Depression is the second most common reason for inability to work in Europe and this costs its joint economies an estimated €120 billion per annum.

Yet the mere statistics of depression speak nothing of the human cost: the pain and suffering of millions of people who struggle daily with a condition that medical science is able only to minimally alleviate and cannot cure. This is the real cost of depression.

❖

"Please God, Let Her Be Alive…"

The roots of my depression run deep into my childhood, back as far as age four. But one cause in particular stands out. It began on a summer Saturday when I was eight years old.

"Would you take Debs to the park for an hour or so?" Mum asked. "I need to do some housework, and it would be helpful if you could get her out of my hair for a while."

I felt elated and joyous as I pushed the old-fashioned baby buggy up the street. Inside it, underneath a white crocheted blanket, was my ten-month-old sister. Her blue eyes shone as she smiled the cutest front-teeth-only smile. I felt ten feet tall.

I'd been trusted with the care of 'my baby sister', and my eight-year-old heart swelled with pride at the thought of showing her off to my friends and neighbors who would undoubtedly be hanging out at the park and playground on such a sunny summer's day. I imagined their delight and their loving approval.

As I looked down at her face, Debs' smile, so innocent and trusting, sparked something in me. It made me want more: more connection, more joy maybe, and I pulled a silly face, poked my tongue out at her. She giggled. I did it again and she burbled out loud with laughter.

I know, I thought; let's play a game of peek-a-boo. Debs always loves that.

I pushed the buggy, let go of the handle and let it go a couple of steps ahead, so Debs lost sight of me, then I quickly caught up and surprised her with a silly face, thumbs stuck in my ears, fingers wiggling, tongue out. "Boo!" I exclaimed.

She loved it. Her smile widened and she chortled away; it was the best game ever. With each push the buggy went a little farther away from me and I took a couple more steps and a little longer to catch up and surprise her with the peek-a-boo. Soon I was pushing her away quite hard. Neither of us had a care in the world.

We turned a corner onto the slope down to the park. I pushed the buggy ahead and ran to catch it up, but I had miscalculated. The buggy was too far ahead and out of control. I ran as fast as I could, but it was hopeless. I stopped, frozen in terror, as the buggy raced down the hill, veered to the right, hit a curbstone, catapulted head-over-heels and crashed upside down into the base of a huge chestnut tree.

In that stunning, traumatic second my whole body flooded through with the terrifying thought, 'I've killed my sister!'

I blurted out loud, 'Dear God… please let her be alive! If you do, I promise I will never do that again.'

I ran full pelt down the road. The blanket lay underneath the upturned buggy, on the grass. I peered underneath, expecting blood, carnage. There was none.

I gently pulled the buggy right ways up. As it righted, Debs stayed fixed inside. Her harness had been invisible underneath the blanket. My mum had secured her into the buggy.

Debs was unmarked, unharmed, and her smile was huge. She laughed out loud, like this was the best, most exciting adventure ever. If she could have spoken, I'm sure she would have said, "More!" or "Again!" And she was alive. She was safe.

My body flooded through with fear and guilt as I checked around me. I picked up the blanket and covered her over once more, made sure she was comfortable. Were there any adults about? Did anyone see? Was I in serious trouble?

There was no one: no one to tell on me, no one to berate or punish me. We continued to the playground. I gripped the buggy's handle like I was glued to it, plodding, in a haze, Debs still beaming, enjoying the ride.

At the park friends gathered around to admire, coo and ah at the baby. I stood by, almost mute, feeling disembodied and distant. An hour passed and we extra-carefully returned home.

"How was the park?" asked Mum.

"Fine."

"And Debs? How was she?"

"Fine."

Mum undid the harness and picked Debs up, cuddled her and took her into the kitchen for feeding. I went out to our backyard and half-heartedly kicked some stones around, not sure what to do with myself.

A sense of secret guilt and 'badness' lurked in the background and unsettled me. I tried in my own childish way to process what had happened, to resolve the tumult I was feeling, understand its importance or relevance, pigeonhole the event and safely tuck it away at the back of my mind. But I couldn't figure it out, couldn't find any thoughts that made the distressing wrangle of feelings go away. All I could come back to was that Debs wasn't hurt, and everything should be okay, but it wasn't.

Though Debs was fine and suffered no ill effects from our mishap, for me the trauma of the incident, and the vow it drew from me, caused an emotional shutdown that became a significant root cause of the depression that I experienced for the next 30 years.

The Shutdown

What my body really wanted to do, as I kicked stones in the yard, was break down and sob, to empty out the stored shock and pain, to ask for and receive forgiveness. My body as well as my mind wanted to know that everything was okay, that Debs was safe and unharmed, and that I could relax knowing life would continue as normal. But I froze, silently shut down and suppressed the instinctive fear that had been triggered. I braced against my feelings. And as time went on I continued to keep things under wraps, pretending that I was 'fine', that there was no issue. I faked it.

Over time my mind forgot, but my body did not. My body held on to vestiges of the memory, residues of its rampant but stuck emotional chemistry - the chemistry of the initial dread that I had killed my sister - and stored them in my cells. Unknowingly, I physically hung onto this unresolved trauma, one that had not healthily played itself out to emotional completion, and my body created a 'cell memory,' the effects of which would come back to haunt me for decades.

My Vow

In that dreadful, panicked, instant when I was terrified that I had killed Debs I made a mistake that any of us might have made. In the face of overwhelming fear, I tried to do a deal with God, with life, without realizing what my end of that deal meant or what it would lead to.

I shouted out a promise to God, made a desperately potent vow: 'If you save her, I will never do that again.' In that moment I didn't, of course, stop to consider what 'that' actually was. In my young mind, I suppose, I meant that I would never again act dangerously, recklessly, would never be out of control or irresponsible, that I would never again risk my sister's safety. And because she was saved the vow was concretized, the deal struck. I had to keep my side of the bargain.

I now see that the promise gained an energy of its own, it became generalized and spread to unintended areas of my life, had unforeseen consequences. Like a pebble dropped in pond it made ripples that reached far and wide. As time went on, 'that' came to include being playful, silly and childish, it included being joyous, excited, spontaneous or too happy, and none of them were allowed.

I came to believe that play, silliness, frivolity, letting go, all equaled death, or at least the risk of death. At a deep and unconscious level I believed that if I did not behave responsibly someone would be harmed or perish, and it would be my fault. These beliefs fed into, and reinforced the shutdown that had already taken place, and my habit of emotional avoidance and suppression began.

Although the memory of the vow got buried somewhere deep at the back of my mind, and I was consciously unaware of my limiting beliefs, I quickly turned into a mini-adult, or what I imagined an adult should be: serious, withheld, measured and responsible, in control of my own emotions and my behavior. For me, this was the thin end of the wedge of depression.

A few years ago Debs turned 50, and our family celebrated with a large dinner party. An old home movie was played. It included footage of Debs' christening day, a big family celebration that took place some three months before the accident. As proud parents and grandparents, each dressed in their mid-1960s Sunday-best outfits, looked on and posed with the little center of attraction, a young boy played.

As I watched the grainy silent movie I felt tears rising in emotional recognition of an innocent time. I was looking at a long-forgotten version of myself; carefree, running, jumping, skipping, light-heartedly playing as the adults spoke to each other and self-consciously mouthed unheard words to the camera.

It was poignant to realize that only a few months later the picture would have been very different and that little boy would become dour, contained and detached, as if the spark of childhood playfulness had been extinguished and the mantle of responsible and world-weary adulthood had been placed on his small shoulders. By the time spring turned into summer I would already be shutting down emotionally, and inadvertently heading for depression.

Life's experiences would trigger me many times during the ensuing years. Many more factors, more episodes, would add to the weightiness and restrictive, overbearing sense of responsibility I felt in life. Some periods were better, some worse; some were extremely painful. And it all started here.

As we go together through this book I'll be sharing more of my own story which, I hope will bring emotional resonance for you, a sense of 'me too'. I trust that this will help you to feel empowered to recognize some of the upsets or traumas that occurred in your own life, maybe during childhood or maybe later in life, and furthermore to realize that the past absolutely can be healed.

Before we get to the practical work in the book I'd like to take some time to explore what depression is and bust a few myths about it.

CHAPTER 2

Busting the Myths of Depression

The term depression covers a large spectrum of experiences and its meaning is often unclear or confusing. But how we frame and approach depression is vital to our ability to successfully change, clear it, free ourselves from it.

To understand what depression really is, it helps to describe some of its symptoms. Doing so can help you to recognize what you or those around you currently experience or have experienced in the past. Please note that this is by no means a comprehensive list and is not meant to clinically diagnose depression.

So, starting with mild depression, what are some of the conditions we encounter?

Symptoms of Mild Depression

With mild or low level depression we may experience restlessness or a general dissatisfaction with our circumstances. We may sense that something is off balance or needs to change in our lives, even though we may not be clearly aware what the problem is. We may feel 'down' or 'blue'; we may feel a disconnection with other people or with life, feel lackluster, low in energy, listless or tired. Our goals or aspirations in life can lose their potency or become vague, and our ability to take charge, to make happen and change our circumstances, slips out of our grip. Our behavior often gets more passive, and we become somewhat negative or cynical about life's challenges and even its opportunities. At this level there may also be some ill-defined anxiety, background nervousness or a feeling of being ill-at-ease with life. We may begin to feel lethargic and sleep more, or to experience difficulty sleeping and lie awake fretting and worrying. We may start eating more and putting on weight, or watching more television, or habitually playing video games instead of getting outdoors, walking or going to the gym. Sometimes there may be a sense of 'caring less' or a sense that something is not quite right, is 'off' in ourselves or in life.

These low-level symptoms of depression can commonly come and go. They may last for days or weeks at a time; they can last for years or even decades. But they also can disappear, and often do when there is a positive shift in, say, our relationships, home environment, career or financial circumstances. We can more easily talk or act ourselves out of this level of depression than we can the deeper, more serious levels. For most people, though, the likelihood is that at some point, like the reappearance of some embarrassing or tiresome old friends, the symptoms will eventually return. It is not inevitable that the pattern will deteriorate. It may stay at this level, but if it worsens our symptoms will get more acute.

Symptoms of Moderate Depression

Our dissatisfaction and restlessness can deepen into real sadness, emptiness and a sense of loss, or of being lost. Life may begin to appear pointless or meaningless, and we can develop a sense of purposelessness. We may become more withdrawn socially, avoiding friends and hunkering down at home. Our sex drives may reduce and we might begin to shun intimacy. A sense of victimhood can begin to grow and make us feel that we are puppets and life is cynically pulling our strings.

At this moderate level we may begin to experience the 'blanket' of depression, as if we have insulated ourselves from life's pains by covering ourselves with thick, dense or fuggy layers of energetic protection. We may feel numb or narcotized to life, as if nothing can really reach us or touch us because we have metaphorically medicated ourselves. Or we may start, literally, to self-medicate, eating more comfort foods, drinking more alcohol or using recreational drugs in an attempt to alleviate our discomfort.

Any background sense of anxiety or nervousness may now show itself more prominently, and can lead to mindless, pointless, or rote activities that may distract us from what we are really feeling emotionally. This type of background anxiety may cause us not to eat more, but to lose our appetites, eat less and lose weight.

As this level intensifies we might feel an increasing sense of being trapped, with a growing sense of helplessness or overwhelm. Our focus turns more strongly inwards as we become increasingly absorbed in the battle with our seemingly irresolvable problems. If the pattern continues to deteriorate we might experience a detrimental shift in our awareness that gives rise to the 'Three Ps' of depression, making our problems seem personal, pervasive and permanent. Then a deep-seated sense of powerlessness and hopelessness can follow.

At this stage our bodies can begin to really suffer: our physical energy can plummet, tiredness can seem overwhelming, our hidden insecurities and fears become more explicit and present. Our immune systems can become compromised, causing frequent colds, infections or other illnesses. As symptoms increase, it becomes increasingly difficult to 'pull ourselves together' and find a genuinely positive attitude. It becomes more difficult to find effective, lasting antidotes by changing interests, focus and activities, despite the exhortations of those who care about us.

This moderate level of depression can rise and fall in potency - although, in my own experience, once we have succumbed to it, it rarely seems to disappear completely of its own accord. While our daily experiences can vary significantly in emotional quality, once we have experienced the downward spiral into this level of pain, there always seems to be some awareness of it in the background. Like an implicit threat lurking just out of sight, it can stalk and pounce on us with no apparent notice.

Symptoms of Severe Depression

Again, it is not inevitable that things will get worse. But if they do, life gets even more painful as a shift takes place into severe depression. Here, it can feel like being drawn relentlessly into a deeper darkness. Our existence can seem completely empty, like a void. It can feel like being caught in a whirlpool of negativity from which there is no escape, or like being in a dark tunnel with no light at the end.

We can become disoriented, detached from our surroundings or circumstances, oblivious. Our rote behaviors may disintegrate into frantic or manic 'wheel spinning' as we desperately attempt to avoid facing reality and our painful emotions.

And as we shut down further and collapse deeper inwards a sense of hopelessness or overwhelm can become pervasive.

Our physical health can rapidly deteriorate as we neglect to feed ourselves and fail to take care of our own basic needs. We may begin to self-punish or self-harm. Our bodily functions begin to shut down and our biochemistry gets seriously disrupted. Physical pain increases; our mental functioning deteriorates and can become incapacitated. At the most deteriorated levels we may seriously consider and plan suicide; at worst we may follow through and take our own lives.

Phew! As painful as it is to open with and fully consider these patterns (all of which, with the exception of course of actual suicide, I have in the past experienced), I think it important to acknowledge that the term depression covers a huge spectrum of conditions, from the subtle and barely noticeable 'blues' through the painful and distressing levels of darkness to the excruciating and life-threatening extremes of hopelessness.

To be absolutely clear at this point: this book is aimed at those of us who experience, or have in the past experienced, mild to moderate depression.

The work included here has a long track record of success with this type of condition. It is not aimed at those suffering from the physical and/or mental effects of severe depression. If you suspect or recognize that you are experiencing severe depression, you should get medical help, get properly diagnosed and take the advice you are given. Then, when your condition is properly managed, you may choose to come back and try out some of the exercises and process work included here.

So, from now on, when I refer to depression I will be referring only to the mild to moderate depression such as is described above.

Let's Get Clear About Depression

When I look back over the list of symptoms written here, knowing that this is just a sample and by no means a comprehensive list, what I realize is that none of these descriptions actually define depression. As much as they can evoke the sensations and feelings associated with depression, they don't tell us anything about what, at its essence, it really is.

So, what is depression?

It might help to first get clear about what it is not. So, let's bust four common myths.

#1: Depression is not a mental illness.

I know this is a contentious statement that not everyone will agree with, and it may even make some people angry to read it. I'm sometimes faced with incredulity in workshops when I say it, especially by people who have been diagnosed as having a 'mental illness' called depression, but let me repeat: depression is not in itself a mental illness. There is no known, identifiable mental dysfunction that sits at the core of depression and defines it. There is no valid proof that this is what depression essentially is.

To illustrate this point, just go back to some of the symptoms of mild depression - say, low energy, feeling lackluster, unfulfilled or out of balance in life. You wouldn't call those symptoms indicative of a 'mental illness', would you? Of course not.

Similarly, mental illness does not normally or necessarily cause depression. There is no clinical evidence that mental illness is a prerequisite for the advent of depression. Recent research in the US by a number of scientists actually casts doubt on the link between depression and low serotonin levels, the basic assumption in the labeling of depression as a mental illness, which drives the prescription of massive amounts of so-called 'anti-depression' SSRI drugs such as Prozac, Zoloft and Paxil. It appears that there never was any hard, independent, research-based proof that such a connection exists. It was an assumption made by pharmaceutical companies with huge financial interest in peddling their drugs, drugs originally designed to treat not depression but anxiety.

What it is true to say, however (and there is copious evidence to support this), is that depression can cause a disruption in normal perception and mental processing. Depression, particularly if it is severe, can cause mental dysfunction. It doesn't always do so, but it can.

So, if we approach the treatment of depression by labeling it as a mental illness we fall into the trap of attempting to cure the condition by treating one of its possible side effects. It's like taking antacid tablets to cure a stomach ulcer: it may temporarily alleviate some of the symptoms, but it won't treat the real problem.

#2: Depression is not a physical disease.

Depression is not in the literal medical sense a physical disease. It does not have a specific observable pathology, does not produce specific predictable cellular change, and does not proceed in expression along linear paths. It is neither infectious nor contagious. Calling depression a disease is like calling stress a disease: stress can cause disease or illness, but it is not what stress really is.

Certainly, depression can cause physical ailments and dysfunction. If it is severe enough it can mess with our endocrine systems and cause hormonal imbalances. It can play havoc with our immune systems, making us more susceptible to infections, viruses and other illnesses.

But it is counterproductive to define or even to approach depression as if it, in itself, is a disease or an illness. When we do there is the danger that we divorce ourselves from the real, personal and environmental causes of the condition and begin to see ourselves as a victim of this 'thing'. We might expect that it may be cured with a pill, and it cannot. There is no drug on earth that has been proven effective in curing depression - not one.

#3: Depression is not an emotion.

Depression can feel emotional, or it can feel devoid of emotion. Depending on the level of depression we experience it can be vaguely discomforting or numbed-out and hazy or severely painful - but it is not in itself an emotion. Emotions come and go in our lives; they rise and fall normally, in a matter of a few seconds to a few minutes. If you watch a young child (one too young to have learned any games or strategies of emotional resistance) playing and getting hurt - maybe a playmate says something harsh and rude to them, or they get excluded from a game, or maybe they get a scratch or graze that is emotionally upsetting - what you see is something like this: tears come easily, then turn quickly into anger or grumpiness, then into hurt or sadness, which in turn becomes some sort of lost-ness, or tenderness, then openness... and before long, that child is naturally and happily playing again, freely engaging, feeling whatever else arises in the next moment. They allow their emotions to flow, to move through their bodies and move out. They allow the natural emotional process to complete.

Emotions come and go of their own accord. It is only when we try to manip-ulate them - try to resist, modify or mute them - that we get bogged down and cause ourselves lasting problems. For then we turn our emotions into a mood, and moods can last quite a long time. Then, if we persist with our manipulations, telling ourselves stories justifying our shutdowns, we can progressively turn a mood into a state and ultimately into an emotional condition - and states and conditions can last for months, for years or even for decades.

So depression is not an emotion. It is a state or condition, one that we create by closing down to, resisting or putting to sleep our raw, natural feelings.

#4: Depression is not a genetically inherited inevitability.

During the lead-up to the turn of the millennium enormous sums of money were spent on genetic research and the scheme to map the human genome, hu-mankind's DNA blueprint. The heady goal was to create a model so comprehensive and all-inclusive that it would predict the quality, expression and fate of human life. The plan was to create a scientific 'crystal ball' that would allow a privileged few to peer deep inside us and see what makes us tick. It would be a method to accurately foretell our propensities, our future behaviors and health, including the diseases we would succumb to. Ultimately (to the delight of life insurance actuaries every-where) it was supposed to predict what we would die of, and when.

Eventually, the code was cracked and the human genome was fully mapped, but there was a problem: it predicted very little. The ensuing years were strewn with scientific disappointments as it was realized that human behaviors, habits and health are very difficult to understand and often impossible to model predic-tively. It was quickly discovered that other factors than our gene sequences were in play in determining our biological and medical destiny.

The focus of research shifted as it was seen that the blueprint for human life was only that: a blueprint. And blueprints are simply guidelines; they are suggestions as to how a structure might take shape, not the structure itself. Ultimately, they are metaphors - variable, fluid, and open to interpretation. Hence, in more recent years with the study of what is called epigenetics it has been discovered that the individual genes in our DNA sequences can seemingly randomly switch off and be unexpressed, or switch on and be expressed. In other words, at any given time specific genes or groups of genes can be of influence or of no influence.

As epigenetics research has progressed it has been discovered that although certain behaviors and predilections can be passed on from one generation to the next, it also appears that factors as profoundly simple as our personal beliefs can directly influence the switching on or off of specific genes. The personal choices we make and the way we individually perceive and 'map' our experiences and the world around us directly affect how our genetic make-up responds, the results it produces. Ultimately, we are not bound by or slaves to our genetic inheritance.

Depression, no matter what you might have been told, is not an inevitable legacy handed down from generation to generation. It is never a foregone prognosis. Although our common environments and others' behaviors and attitudes can deeply influence us, depression is never inevitable in anyone's life.

If you are interested, conduct your own Internet research on the topic of depression. Look deeper than the standard references, to some of the current work being done to truly understand depression, and you may be shocked to discover for yourself what I discovered: that depression is not what we commonly believe it to be; it is not what the pharmaceutical companies and the orthodox medical profession have been telling us it is.

So if depression is not any of these things, what might it be? What is it really?

The root of depression is a pattern of emotional shutdown and blocking, a habit designed to protect us from feeling something threatening, undermining or otherwise painful.

The real cause of depression is our unconscious habit of emotional suppression and blocking that is our attempt to turn down the fear, the distress and the pain in our lives. This suppression and blocking is often associated with some form of hurt, trauma or unresolved pain – sometimes from much earlier in our lives.

Over time, our habit of closing down deepens; it becomes ingrained and automatic, and eventually crystallizes into a condition - a condition of emotional shutdown and stuckness. So ultimately depression is a condition of emotional blockage that is born from our desperate and mostly ineffective attempts to keep the bad stuff of life at bay.

I really want to emphasize this point: depression is not an illness or disease - mental or physical - it is essentially, at its core, a condition of emotional suppression.

The huge irony is that, if left unchecked, our habits of internal emotional closure are eventually capable of producing far more pain than they could ever protect us from. Our habits of shutdown and suppression - designed initially to shield us from some hurt, some emotional intensity - become deeply imprinted in us, and then we rely on them ever more pervasively. When they don't make us feel better we unconsciously ramp them up: we do the same thing but more so. We retreat farther inside, create thicker blankets of insulation, and shut down more of our emotional responses. We trap ourselves in an emotional straightjacket of our own making. Then the protection becomes the pain, the antidote becomes the poison, and the condition of depression begins and eventually takes hold.

When I speak about freedom from depression, what I am really talking about is freedom from these unconscious habits, these emotional manipulations. Freedom from the trap of insulation and isolation; freedom from the locked down prison of emotional containment; freedom from the suppression of natural human feelings that eventually causes so much pain. I also mean freedom to live life fully, freedom to feel and express, be authentic and fulfilled. **I also mean freedom to be yourself:** *your real self.*

The ultimate goal is clear: we have to find a way to let go of some of our old restrictive habits and respond more healthily, more wholesomely to life's challenges, dramas and uncertainties. We must learn to allow our emotions to be felt, to flow and naturally to subside. And we must learn to heal from, to come to completion with, past upsets and traumas, whatever they might be. In essence, our challenge is to become more emotionally healthy, so we can feel inherently better about ourselves and about life.

The great news is that Journeywork has already helped many thousands of people worldwide to make profound shifts in these areas of their lives. It is a well tried and tested methodology for personal and emotional transformation.

For the moment all I ask is that you play along. Rather than relying on beliefs or limitations borrowed from others, stay open and true to your own first-hand experience during our upcoming explorations. This will be a theme as we work together, as you try out for yourself the various introspections and techniques included here.

So please let go of your preconceived ideas or beliefs about what is and what is not true, what can and can't help, and stay open to your honest, personal, subjective experience of the work in this book. Your direct experience is what is most important and is key to your own transformation.

So, let's try a little experiment to find out some emotions you may be automatically avoiding in life. We all avoid some of our emotions, and it's important to recognize this fact, and good to know some of the specific ones you personally avoid. To do this, we'll imagine going back to a time when we were emotionally triggered or upset and we'll discover what we were really feeling at that time. You may just get a subtle glimpse of this emotion, or it may be a full recognition, and both are fine. In either case you will probably get a sense of some feeling that arose and was not fully felt, was in some way avoided. Let's explore.

Just for guidance, all of the exercises (sometimes referred to as introspections or processes) will need you to set aside some time. Some you can do whilst you are reading this book, they're quick to do and you can carry on reading. If you choose to work this way remember that whenever you see three dots like this '…' in one of these exercises it means you should make a short pause. For others you'll need to find a quiet space and be ready to relax and then work for longer. These longer introspections are all explained in chapter 9. For the shorter ones I'll give you an indication of how long each one might take and whether you need someone else to support you whilst you allow yourself to explore.

For every exercise you have the option to get online and access the audio recordings I have prepared for you, so you can allow me to personally guide you through the work. That's my best recommendation because then you can just relax and allow your thinking mind to rest as you follow along.

Exercise 1

Instructions: What Were You really Feeling?

Download the audio and script at www.kevinbillett.org/book-bonus

This first introspection doesn't need a lot of time - 5 to 7 minutes should be fine. Just find a quiet place where you can sit and relax without interruptions.

Intention:
That you uncover the real emotions that were triggered in you at a past time of upset

Time:
5 to 7 minutes

Emotional level:
Mildly to moderately emotional

What you need:
Quiet space. Tissues

At the end:
Short break of 5 minutes or so

Exercise 1: What were you really feeling?

Find a comfortable seat, relax and take some long, deep breaths in and out... Then, as you relax and bring your attention to your breathing, just invite your thinking mind to soften, and unwind... let it relax and open... Now let your body relax from head to toe... inside and out... Allow your whole being to come to stillness and rest...

And now, in your mind's eye, just imagine a time when something emotionally triggered you in life... remember a time when something happened, maybe something recent, that really tweaked you or pushed your emotional buttons... It may have been an accident, a drama, an argument or confrontation... or some other circumstance that was emotionally upsetting... Got it?...

Great... So now imagine this memory as a movie track that you can play at any speed you choose. It can forwards or backwards, and can slow right down so you can clearly see and hear what took place...

Now imagine the movie rolling slowly backwards to the point at which you were triggered... to the exact point at which the upset initially occurred... and freeze frame the movie right here...

Just stop the movie and let it rest at the precise moment you were triggered by this circumstance... The split second before you avoided what you were feeling at the deepest level... before you reacted to the circumstance... And imagine opening this moment until it becomes wider and more accessible... Just soften your body and let awareness open deep inside... and begin to sense what you are really feeling emotionally, in the micro-moment before you react to the trigger...

What emotion are you really feeling?... What intense or painful or fearful emotion is here?... It may just be a fleeting glimpse of this feeling, so pay close and sensitive attention to your body... What is the truth of your real emotional response?... Sense deeply inside your body... What emotion was it that you subsequently avoided feeling fully?...

Whisper it out loud... And if there is more than one emotion here, just name whatever arises... it doesn't need to be the exact or perfect word for what you are feeling, just the name you choose for it... Whisper out loud what you are really feeling... And allow your body to feel, to open with and accept whatever is here... Take a moment or two to just be with whatever emotion or emotions are here... And let it eventually naturally subside... Great...

Now come back to neutral and if your eyes closed at any point, of course you can open them... Good. Thank you.

So what did you discover? What emotion or emotions did you recognize? What did you not allow yourself to fully feel at the moment you were triggered emotionally?

Of course, different life circumstances trigger different emotional responses in each of us, so you may want to repeat the exercise above using different memories to discover what you were really feeling and what you were avoiding by your shutdown. You may discover very different emotional responses or you may discover some emotional themes, repeat emotions or groups of emotions that keep recurring. Either result is fine and is normal.

Over the years, whenever I've tried this 'roll the movie back' experiment I have been surprised, sometimes even shocked, at the emotions I was avoiding. I discovered underlying anger, rage, weakness, helplessness, worthlessness, dread, and fear (to name just a small selection) that I had been thoroughly suppressing.

Each time I explored in this way I found an underbelly of emotions that I was unconscious to in normal life. I had no idea that I was really feeling fear, or anger when I reacted with my normal 'no bother' attitude. There was no real clue that my underlying responses to life were so emotional. In fact, I was so used to my habitual emotional shutdowns and they seemed so 'normal' that I had no idea that we humans were routinely such emotional creatures.

We're going on now to look in a lot more detail at our emotions over the next few chapters. My story continues and there are more exercises too.

CHAPTER 3

How Emotions Shape Us

I hope the experiment at the end of the previous chapter helped you to see that we human beings not only feel emotions but that we are not always aware of some of our deeper emotions. We are, in fact, very emotional animals.

During the course of a single day we experience a huge variety of feelings. We might feel happy or excited, hurt or scared, appreciated or loved, embarrassed or uncomfortable, inadequate or unworthy, angry, powerful, jealous or lonely, or any other of a huge list of commonly experienced emotions. The point is that we all feel, and those feelings are vital to us. As much as we might deny or struggle with the fact, we all automatically perceive and respond to life's events in an emotional way.

How we feel is a critical component in how we determine our lives' paths. Our emotions affect our behaviors, our responses, our choices and even our perceptions. We are emotionally driven and emotionally motivated. And emotions ultimately define the quality of our lives: how we feel is the biggest factor in how fabulous or wretched we perceive our lives to be.

All Our Choices Are Ultimately Emotional

Recent brain research shows that at the point of making a decision, at the very instant we choose - be it a major life choice like choosing a partner or deciding where to live, or a minor choice like what clothes we buy or what meal we order in a restaurant - only the emotional part of the brain is used. At the split second we decide, only the limbic part of the brain, the instinctual and emotional processing section, fires up.

After that split second of emotionally driven choice the thinking brain activates to analyze or rationalize our choices, checking them out and running through their possible implications. This analysis can and does modify how we ultimately feel emotionally about our choices. But the bottom line is this: all of our choices are essentially emotional ones.

Shortly after the first iPads had been released, I checked this out for myself and the results astonished me. I did some online research, found out all the features and benefits, and went to the nearest Apple store to see it for myself. I checked the price of the model I wanted, figured that I could use it as an e-reader plus check emails, browse the Internet, etc. I came to what I thought was a sensible, rational and justifiable decision - and I bought one.

Around the same time, I read several books quoting brain research that suggested that all our decisions were essentially emotionally based. The evidence was compelling, but I was still skeptical and decided to check it out for myself.

I closed my eyes and recalled the exact moment when I 'made my mind up' to buy the iPad. Then I rolled the image back to the split second before making the choice, and I felt into the moment, into what emotion or emotions might be present. Then I relaxed deeper and allowed whatever arose to be fully felt.

I imagined being back in the store, with the device in my hands, seeing its shape and size, the colors and sheen on its screen; feeling its weight, its smoothness, the roundness of its edges, its sheer quality. I expected to find that some sound logic, some good, dispassionate reason underpinned my purchase. But that was far from the truth. I was shocked to realize that in the instant before deciding my body was flooded with desire, something akin to lust or yearning. And I felt a longing for the sense of fulfillment I imagined owning the iPad would bring.

In the background, I was aware of feeling some anxiety about spending the amount of money it would cost and about explaining the purchase to my wife, but the fear was overridden completely by the desire. Like a kid in a candy store, I had to have it. The decision to buy was clearly a powerfully emotional one. I hadn't 'made my mind up' at all; my emotions had made my mind up for me!

We Justify Our Emotional Decisions With Thinking

In my mind's eye I let the scene play forward, and noticed something interesting. In the seconds after I made the decision, my thinking mind kicked back in, and did a wonderful job of justifying my choice, producing many 'reasons' why my choice was a good one, the right one. My thoughts reinforced a feeling of satisfaction, of ease and peace with the choice I had made. My thinking did not produce the decision or cause it to be made; instead, post-event it confirmed a decision that had been emotionally generated.

I realized that this purchase was a simple choice, not one of huge significance in my life, so I continued to explore. I checked back in the same way with other life decisions I had at one time or another made: choosing relationship partners, making business decisions, deciding where to vacation, where to live. The results were the same. In each case it was ultimately an emotion or a set of emotions that drove me to choose one thing over another, to say yes instead of no, or vice versa.

Sometimes, in the moments after deciding, my mind confirmed the choice, and at other times it questioned the choice, confusing matters, making me feel differently and delaying things. And in each case, when the final choice was made, it was driven exclusively by my emotions. It was my emotions that made me say 'yes'.

Then I noticed that I had focused only on decisions in life where I said yes, where I made a proactive choice, a decision to do something. I began to wonder if there was a different process for deciding not to do something. I stopped and imagined going back in time, open to what might show up. What arose was a memory of being 18 years old, just finishing school. I had the idea that I would take a gap year to travel before going to university. The more I thought about it the more compelling the idea seemed; I'd go to Australia and New Zealand where I'd work and surf during my year off. I would have fun and 'get the travel bug out of my system' before knuckling down to another three years of study.

I spoke to my best friend, Pete, and attempted to convince him that this was a great idea. I used every argument I could muster as to why he should go with me, why it would be a life-changer, why it was a must, but he was not interested. Deflated, I retreated and reconsidered. Eventually I gave up the dream, didn't make the trip, and went straight to university.

I took this memory into the same process of enquiry. Again I rolled the cameras back to the split-second before I made the choice to not follow through, to say no to the gap year. I opened, I stopped resisting, and welcomed the emotions I had felt at that time, and again was surprised.

In that moment before deciding my body was awash with feelings, many of them conflicting: excitement at the prospect of adventure and meeting new people, of golden beaches warm seas and pristine waves; uplift at the thought of escaping the responsibility and the humdrum weight of further study; worry at the realization that I would need more money than I had currently saved. But the dominant emotion? Pure fear at the prospect of traveling around the world on my own. Pure fear at the thought of knowing no one and of stepping alone into the unknown. Fear, plain and simple, drove the decision to say no, to pull back and miss out on a year that could have positively impacted the whole course of my life.

So my direct inquiries verified what I had read. As surprising as it was, I discovered for myself that the scientific research was true. For better or for worse, our decisions - from the simplest and least consequential to the biggest and most impactful - are driven by our emotions.

As I read more and deeper research I learned that the scientists, who performed these tests by wiring up volunteers' brains to sophisticated scanning machines while they asked them to make choices, initially doubted their own findings. So they found different volunteers, people who had suffered some brain damage that left their rational intelligence intact but disrupted their ability to feel and process emotions effectively. Their IQs were still what they had always been, but their feelings had been compromised, or were unreachable.

When they asked these volunteers to make some choices the results were stunning. The test patients retreated with notebooks and pens, made long lists of pros and cons - and could not make decisions. Asked even simple questions like, 'Would Tuesday or Thursday suit you better for our next appointment?' the volunteers elaborately contemplated why one might be better than the other, and they could not decide, no matter how long they pondered. There was no emotional connection, no emotional weight to the questions, so no choice was convincingly available, no decision could be made.

When our emotions are not available to us, either because of some brain trauma or, maybe, because we have shut them down or suppressed them, our decision-making abilities are severely compromised. Without feelings we are unable to decide and be confident or satisfied with our choices.

Let's try another experiment here, to find out how your own decision-making is driven by your emotions. I find in life that if something is not true in my own direct experience, then it might as well not be true, so check this out for yourself.

Instructions: What Shapes Your Decisions?

Download the audio and script at www.kevinbillett.org/book-bonus

You can treat this as an eyes open and eyes closed introspection, opening them to read a little then gently closing to inquire and experience. Or you could ask someone you trust to softly read out the words to you as you keep your eyes closed. The exercise will take only about 10 to 12 minutes, so if you wish you can do it right now. Just find a quiet space to work in.

Intention:
That you discover how emotions really shape and drive your decisions in life
Time:
10 to 12 minutes
Emotional level:
Mildly emotional
What you need:
Quiet space
At the end:
Short break of 5 minutes or so

Exercise 2: What shapes your decisions?

Close your eyes and take a few slow, deep breaths as you relax and let awareness turn inside your body.

Ask your thinking mind to relax and wind down, like a ceiling fan whose power has been switched off. Let awareness sink deeply inside your body... Let it slowly slide down into your chest, and heart... your stomach... your belly... relaxing more deeply with each breath... with each sensation you feel.

Now, in your mind's eye, imagine being effortlessly transported, wafted back in space and time to a time and place when you made a significant life decision, preferably one you still feel good about. It could be when you said yes to a date, or a relationship, or even chose a life partner... it could be when you chose a job or a career... it could be when you decided to live in a particular place or when you chose a specific home... It could be a time when you chose some lovely clothes, a car, a vacation or some equipment... It could be when you chose to bring home a pet... Or it could be any other time when you decided to take action, to do something proactive or decisive in life. Any one of these is fine, even if it is not yet fully clear to you...

Just allow yourself to be carried back to any scene... any moment. Seeing the picture of the environment and the people who were there... hearing the sounds of speaking, of background noises, or your own internal dialogue... and feeling the sensations and emotions that were present at that time...

And now slow things down and gently bring them just to the point at which you decide... to the exact moment the choice is made... and pause there... Now make a miniscule adjustment, and let the scene go back and settle at the instant before you make the decision, to the split second prior to choosing... And let your sense of this tiny slice of time expand and open... Let your body relax as you let this moment, this millisecond before you decide, get bigger and wider...

Let all awareness in to this slice of time... Open with, and rest in what you are feeling... What are you feeling emotionally?... Just allow this feeling to naturally arise... be present... and be felt. What feeling is here? Whisper it out: what emotion are you feeling?

What else are you feeling?... Just open a little wider or deeper and check... what else is here... what other feelings or emotions are present? And just allow them... welcome them to be felt... Now inquire, which of these is the strongest emotion, which is the most important, the biggest or the most dominant?... And now welcome that specific emotion to be fully present... welcome it to be really felt.

Now ask: If this emotion were allowed to be fully felt, what impulse arises with it? As you fully welcome this feeling to be present, notice - what action does it trigger or drive? What does it want or even require you to do? What choice becomes obvious or unavoidable? Whisper it out: What action or choice does this emotion bring with it?... Okay, great.

Now come to neutral and let go of that memory and those feelings. Just loosen your body and imagine a neutral space... Allow awareness to give rise to a time when you made a decision not to do something, when you held back on something you may have wanted to do, when you neglected to say yes or braced and decided to say no. Maybe this was a time when you failed to do something and later regretted it, a time when you might have made a healthier or more self-supportive decision than you did. This could *be a circumstance where you could have reached out and connected with someone you were attracted to, but didn't... where you could have applied for or accepted a job promotion... where you might have made a healthy stretch or taken a healthy risk in life, but decided not to... It could be a time when you wanted to break out of the norm, free yourself from the routine of daily living, but didn't take the necessary action... Or it could be any other time, when you held back and played small rather than fully engaging with life... any one of these is fine, even if it is not yet fully clear to you...*

In your mind's eye, allow yourself to gently be guided back to that time... to the circumstances and the memory relating to that decision...

Just allow yourself to be carried back to that scene... that moment. Seeing the picture of the environment and the people who were there... hearing the sounds of speaking, of background noises, or your own internal dialogue... and feeling the sensations and emotions that were present at that time...

Now slow things down and gently bring them to the point at which you decide... to the exact moment the choice is made... and pause there... Now make a miniscule adjustment, and let the scene go back and settle at the instant before you make the decision, to the split second prior to choosing... And let your sense of this tiny slice of time expand and open... Let your body relax as you let this moment, this millisecond before you decide, get bigger and wider...

Let all awareness in rest in what you are feeling... What are you feeling emotionally?... Just allow this feeling to naturally arise... be present... and be felt. What feeling is here? Whisper it out: what emotion are you feeling?

And what else are you feeling?... Just open a little wider or deeper and check... what else is here... what other feelings or emotions are present? And just allow them... welcome them to be felt... Now inquire, which of these is the strongest emotion, which is the most important, the biggest or the most dominant?... And now welcome that specific emotion to be fully present... welcome it to be really felt.

Now ask: If you allowed this emotion to be fully felt, what impulse arises with it?... As you fully welcome this feeling to be present, notice, what action does it trigger or drive? What does it want or even require you to do? What choice becomes obvious or unavoidable? Whisper it out: What action or choice does this emotion bring with it?... Okay, great.

Now softly allow awareness to come back to the present moment... and place... And you can take a good, long deep breath in... and let it out... And you can open your eyes when you are ready.

What did you discover? What emotions did you uncover, and what do you realize as a result? Are you beginning go see that emotions - both those you want to feel and those you want to avoid feeling - are shaping and influencing forces in our lives?

Take a few moments right now, and sit still. Relax, let go of all thoughts and simply 'be'. Now just feel what is happening in your body, and let any realizations that want to arise be present. Then we can move on.

You Can't Think Your Way Out of Depression

We've acknowledged that we are emotional creatures and discovered that emotions underpin our choices, drive our decisions, make us say yes or no in life. In other words they fundamentally influence our behaviors and habits. We've also discovered that although thinking (that is, adding a meaning to, or changing the meaning about a circumstance) can quickly affect the way we feel about that situation, thinking alone does not enable us to make clear decisions in life. Thinking alone cannot cause us to act healthily or to change our unhealthy actions. To choose healthily, to behave healthily, to live healthily we must be able to feel healthily.

This is really important. Consider the onset of depression: imagine going back to an early time when you remember feeling its uncomfortable symptoms. When you recognized that something was 'off' or unsettling, that things were uncomfortable or disturbing or painful, how did you react? What did you do? Take a moment right now to stop, relax and remember. Let your awareness go back in time. At that time, what was your first response?

If you are like me and like most other people, you thought about it. You tried to analyze your circumstances, sought to quantify or explain the problems you were facing, you rationalized your situation or you tried to figure out what was causing your distress, tried to understand it in an attempt to resolve it or feel better about it.

And this is a core problem. Thinking, especially thinking about emotionally laden problems like depression, normally does not help - in fact, it is often counterproductive. It leads to more thinking, circular thinking, possibly to relentless or compulsive thinking - for instance thinking about who is to blame, how we are being victimized, or how unfair or overwhelming or impossible our circumstances are.

And, far from resolving our situations and making us feel better, this type of inner storytelling often creates internal confusion and turmoil, and robs us of the ability to take clear purposeful action. Over-reliance on thinking can distort our natural emotional health to the point where we become incapacitated, unable to make and follow through with the healthy, self-supportive decisions that success-ful living requires of us.

Turning Emotions Into Life Stories Creates Suffering

Our habitual thinking about, or analyzing of, our problems and our emotional responses to them turns into a story about our lives and the emotions we feel. And although these stories can seem compelling and real, in truth they are merely internal dialogues based on our, often unrecognized, fears. They are primarily a strategy to manage our feelings.

And there is another potential problem with this strategy. When we add a negative or restrictive story to our emotions, as well as creating inner turmoil, we turn those pure flowing emotions into moods or states - and moods and states have a tendency to stick around. If we persist long enough with our stories, and begin to believe they are the truth we can eventually create an emotional condi-tion - maybe even the emotional condition called depression - that can last a very long time!

This is an important point, and one worth reiterating: an emotion can pass through your body in a short period of time and, fully felt, will leave you feel-ing refreshed, cleared out, released. Any emotion that is welcomed and is fully embraced will do this, no matter how powerful or painful it may seem. However, an emotion plus a story about it - about the circumstances that triggered it, the people who caused it or the imagined consequences of feeling it - will turn that emotion into a mood that can last. And by adding a story into our moods we can lock ourselves into a state, or we can eventually create a condition, and states and conditions stick with us and generally take far longer to lift or clear.

Our stories about our emotions are as individual as we are. They may be very evident to us, or they may be so subtle as to be barely recognized, and we all have them. We all have beliefs and rules about what we are 'allowed' to feel and what we are not, about what is appropriate or inappropriate emotionally, or about what is 'good' or 'bad' to feel. We all have our own stories about what is too scary to ever be felt. You've read about some of mine: the stories about being out of control, of feeling too much excitement, silliness or joy. What are some of yours?

Instructions: Your Stories About Emotions

Download the audio and script at www.kevinbillett.org/book-bonus

The next activity will help you to answer that question. There's no need to make a list of everything you identify. As each emotion and story emerges just speak it out, quietly, like you did in the last exercise. Let yourself hear your emotions and their stories and recognize the effect they have. When you've finished the exercise pause for a few minutes, just sit and relax or get a glass of water, and come back to your reading when you are ready.

Intention:
That you discover what stories you have attached to some emotions
Time:
10 to 12 minutes
Emotional level:
Mildly to moderately emotional
What you need:
Quiet space. Tissues
At the end:
Short break of 5 minutes or so

Exercise 3: Your stories about emotions

Take a moment to be still and enquire: What stories about emotions do you have? What is it unsafe to ever feel? What is it 'wrong' to feel? What are you never allowed to feel? And what do you tell yourself to justify these beliefs? What stories do you have, what 'because…' do you hold onto that makes it this way?

If you like, you could close your eyes, ask your thinking mind to relax and rest and then place your attention deep inside your body. Ask your body to reveal the truth. What are your stories about the emotions you avoid? Do you blame others, or circumstances or life itself for the fact that these emotions arise? Do you tell yourself that you are a victim of your emotions, that you are not in control of them and that they will overwhelm you if you open to them? Or do you tell yourself the story that you must resist your emotions at *all costs? What is your version of this game? Just take a few minutes to close your eyes and contemplate, and be willing to let the answers bubble up from somewhere deep inside you. What are some of your habitual stories?*

And how does it make you feel emotionally when you tell yourself these stories? What is their effect on your mood, your state?

If you are like me, these stories might make you feel stuck. They evoke and enhance negativity inside me when I engage with them or choose to believe them. When I choose to stop telling myself these types of stories my emotions arise and fall away quickly, but when I perpetuate the stories I can create some fairly negative moods that tend to hang around.

Most people would tell us to just 'change our thinking', as if that is an easy thing to do. But for any of us who have the habit of creating negative or self-undermining stories, it is an almost impossible task to just choose to be positive, to simply drop our habits. But there is a way to free yourself. **The rarely understood thing about negative thinking is that it is automatically driven by emotions we are - consciously or unconsciously - seeking to avoid.** And the great paradox is that in unearthing and openly feeling those avoided emotions, the way we will do later in the book, our negative stories seem to resolve, finish and fall away. The great beauty of this approach is that we then uncover our own innate positivity, our own natural wellbeing and can live with it in ease.

So, we often figure that in order to solve the problem of depression we need to change our habitually negative thinking, while missing the fact that such thinking is driven by, often caused by our attempts to avoid our natural feelings. In order to free ourselves from unhealthy thinking we must learn to change our unhealthy manipulations of our feelings. We must learn afresh to feel openly, cleanly and fully.

With depression, more thinking is not the solution; instead, it is often a significant part of the problem. Depression is an emotional issue and our thinking is no antidote. Analyzing depression can never alone cure depression.

The antidote to depression is emotional openness and feeling. To fully and finally clear depression we need to get to its emotional root causes, its emotional drivers, and resolve them. We need to change our deeply ingrained beliefs about what emotions are and what they mean, and we must practice a new way of being with our emotions, develop a new and healthy relationship with them. And that is, by definition, an emotional process. It is an emotional process that this book will help you with.

So let's go on to explore what an emotion really is, and how we create behaviors that shut them down.

CHAPTER 4

Manipulating Our Emotions Has Consequences

We humans have evolved the ability to willfully change or manipulate our normally triggered emotions - to feel them in a moderated, more controlled way or to avoid them altogether. Then we forgot that we were playing an emotional 'game' with ourselves, and that forgetting eventually caused us deep-seated problems.

An emotion is a natural human reaction to an event or events. A biochemical response is triggered in our bodies changing our physical energy and chemistry and the sensations we feel inside our bodies. Left to its own devices almost any emotion will, in a short space of time, automatically flow: opening, deepening, intensifying, diffusing, lightening, flooding and washing through the body until it is finished and the next feeling eventually arises.

Emotions in themselves are no problem. As Brandon loves to say, "Emotions come and emotions go. If you don't touch them they burn a 'clean ash'." What that means is that when we allow our pure emotions to arise and be fully felt, without interfering with them or adding any story or meaning to them, they pass cleanly and leave no residue. Our real problem lies in the fact that we have forgotten how to naturally feel our emotions and let them subside of their own accord. We have forgotten how to let them be. Instead we suppress them, block them, put them to sleep, run from them or fight with them - we manipulate our emotions in an attempt to avoid, manage or control them. We normally do anything except actually fully feeling them.

Over hundreds of thousands, maybe millions of years, human brains have evolved and developed some phenomenal capacities. In the face of threat, our brains are hard-wired to automatically respond with 'fight, freeze or flight' responses. These are reflex knee-jerk reactions that we share with many other animals - where we instantly react to potentially dangerous circumstances in ways that maximize our chance of survival; literally, fighting, stopping dead in our tracks or running away. These reactions are not a problem.

But we evolved a different style of emotional control that can and does cause us problems. We learned that by thinking, using rationale, we could willfully change our emotional responses to life's circumstances.

Our forebears discovered how to physically brace against or override fear so they could hunt more effectively, and they learned to shut down or swallow anger and reduce the risk of attack from more dominant members of the tribe. They learned to brace against hurt and pain, to suppress weakness and vulnerability, to harden against incompetence and unlovability, and thus they could feel safer or more included in the tribe. Over time humans learned to change, modify or shut down almost any emotional response that could compromise them or cause them social disadvantage.

We discovered, for example, that a personal slight could be reframed as humor and the potential hurt turned into levity. Or a personal rejection may be viewed as unimportant, or perpetrated by a fool, and the feeling of humiliation might be transmuted into indifference, a much more comfortable feeling.

We developed the ability, at least temporarily, to override and control and manipulate what we were feeling. And within this ability lies a key to our thriving as a species but also a key to our emotional demise, because emotional manipulation produces unintended consequences - in my experience it is the genesis of depression.

The Why and How of Emotional Shut Down

As we have seen, most animals' brains and neurology are hardwired to avoid threat and danger. Many higher forms of life, including humans, have instinctive functions that trigger them automatically to move away from pain and towards pleasure. But humans have a rare ability. Because we have such well-developed thinking capacities we apply rationality to our emotional experiences, to calculate 'intelligently' what we want and how to get it.

So we instinctively apply discernment to our emotional lives. We realize that each emotion produces a distinct sensation in the body, and that some sensations are enjoyable, pleasurable - like feeling confident, powerful, valuable, worthy, competent, admired, loved, in control - and that some are uncomfortable, or painful - like feeling weakness, vulnerability, unworthiness, unlovability, insecurity, shame, humiliation and fear. Naturally, by all means available to us, we seek more pleasure and less pain.

We increasingly use our talents for internal emotional manipulation to avoid what we find painful or uncomfortable, and to seek and enhance what is pleasurable. We've learned to suppress, cover over, hide from and change what we are feeling. Metaphorically as well as literally, we run away from our fears and feared emotions, and we move towards what we think will cause us to feel pleasure. We use our minds to change what we feel by tampering with our natural emotional reactions. We know not only how to moderate what we are feeling, but how to pretend, how to fake it.

Then we learn to judge our own emotions. We label them 'good' or 'bad', and we develop layers of beliefs about what we are allowed to feel, what is good to feel, and what is dangerous or bad to feel. We adopt rules that dictate emotional shoulds, musts and cannots. We tie ourselves up in knots of emotional resistance and stuckness rather than simply stopping, opening and feeling.

And as a result of our mental-emotional manipulations we experience unintended consequences in two distinct yet interconnected ways. The first is that, unlike many other animals, we have lost our ability to literally shake off fear.

Have you ever seen movies of animals hunted by predators - say, an antelope that has been pursued by and has outrun a lion? When the chase is over, if the movie sequence continues, you might notice that the antelope will stand and robustly shake all over. This is not like a dog choosing to shake itself dry, but is an involuntary response that allows the body's fear chemistry to be dispelled and resolve. The adrenaline and cortisol that triggered the flight and fuelled the necessary speed to escape needs to work its way through the antelope's body, and this is how that happens. Within a short few minutes the antelope's fear chemistry has healthily dissipated and it returns to normal grazing.

Humans have in large part lost this function. Our mental-emotional avoidance games mean that our natural emotions often don't healthily flood through the body and release; instead they produce a chemistry that sticks, lingers at a background level and can cause long-term problems for our wellbeing. Numerous clinical researchers in the fields of psycho-neuro-immunology and cellular biology have illustrated the links between emotional suppression and 'phantom' or 'cell' memories, in other words blocked cellular energy that can in the long term create emotional and physical health problems.

The second unintended consequence is this: we forgot that overriding our emotions was always a temporary expedient for use only in the moment of real threat. By repeatedly avoiding our strong emotions we turned a technique into a habit. Then we forgot that we were emotionally shutting down, and we forgot that there ever was another more natural option available to us. It became 'normal' for us to avoid our real feelings. In other words, we learned to emotionally fake it, then we forgot that we were faking it.

So to a significant and damaging extent, we have lost the ability to allow some important natural emotions to arise, be fully experienced and then healthily subside. We all fall into the trap of habitually manipulating our naturally occurring emotions. But if we are all in this same 'avoidance boat' how come only some of us experience depression, when many of us clearly do not?

To answer that question we need to examine how we manipulate our uncomfortable emotions. First we will look at the big picture of our general strategies of avoidance, then we will get more detailed and look at some of the specific techniques we use. This examination is key to understanding the 'why' of depression.

How We Avoid Uncomfortable Emotions

Our general strategies to avoid our deeper feelings fall into three distinct categories called Inflation, Rigidity and Deflation.

These categories are closely associated with our individual personality or character. They are shaped by our personal 'stories' and beliefs about who we are and how we need to behave or appear in order to get by in life.

Although everyone is capable of playing all three of these emotional games, each of us has a favorite, a default or habitual choice that we rely on more than any other; we have a second favorite, our fallback position maybe when our first strategy is not working so well; and we have a third choice, a last resort that we more rarely rely on.

Inflation

The first is the strategy of inflation, and it plays out in a variety of ways. Inflation is a bit like a balloon that has been overfilled, pumped up too much or over primed. It means that our game is one of 'bigging it up', pretending that things are better than they are, that we are coping better or feeling better than we really are. We may inflate our sense of position and self-importance, or our sense of control and autonomy in the world. We may pretend that we are above normal people's problems, that our own fears and insecurities don't exist, that we 'haven't a care in the world'.

We may develop habits such as blame, bullying, aggressiveness, and domination. We may exaggerate our own successes and boast about our strength and our wins. We also may become habitual extraverts, always joshing and joking around, anecdote telling, sharing pop wisdom and emotional quick fixes with others, and reframing circumstances so they don't appear so bad and we can be lighter hearted about them. Or we may exaggerate our sense of self-worth, or personal nobility, and reinforce our self-image of emotional togetherness by habitually sympathizing with others' plights, pridefully caretaking them and tending to their perceived needs while denying our own insecurities.

Habits of inflation lead to an externalization of our own issues, as if they are someone else's problem or some other person's fault, almost as if they are nothing to do with us. But although inflation causes other types of difficulty and pain in life, it does not normally directly lead to depression. For this book's purposes it is enough to know that such strategies exist, then we can allow our focus to go elsewhere, to the two emotional games with direct links to depression.

Rigidity

The second strategy is one of rigidity. Here our emotions are kept on a tight leash: we set boundaries and limits, and we have firm rules about moral or ethical rightness and wrongness. We have beliefs about the 'appropriateness' of feelings and we keep them locked in a straightjacket. We tend to be highly-strung, uptight, inflexible, and nervous or anxious. With rigidity we see withholding, tenseness, formulas, tension, anxiety, stoicism, efficiency, wheel spinning, willful stubbornness, active resistance, self-righteousness and perfectionism. We see the need to 'get it right' in life, to do a good job or to pretend that we are doing a good job.

Our strategies of rigidity lead to emotional resistance: we physically or mentally brace, harden, shut down or block our emotions, sometimes even denying that we are feeling anything at all. We steel ourselves and create barricades to protect us against unwanted feelings as if they are some external force attacking us, or we brace internally against them as if they are some threatening or alien energy inside our bodies that must be protected against at all costs. We harden physically internally and externally against the emotions we do not want to feel and, again, we tell ourselves stories, this time in an attempt to stonewall our real emotions.

Habitual rigidity and the resistance it leads to can feed into depression; it can cause us to live in a perpetual state of tension or stress, and it can be a major influence in what is known as anxiety depression - when depression is infused with fears, nervousness and anxieties. With rigidity we can hold back our normal emotions for so long that eventually it might feel like there is an emotional dam about to break. But rigidity on its own is not the root cause of most depression. Rigidity normally has to combine with a different strategy in order to create depression.

To find the main, the most potent, cause of depression we need to look at that third type of strategy - deflation.

Deflation

Deflation is the opposite of inflation. With this strategy it seems that someone has let all the air out of our balloon and it has shriveled and collapsed. We sink inwards or hunker down and attempt to protect our emotional selves by retreating and withdrawing from social contact, by 'hiding in our shells' or building thick energetic walls around us that keep us deeply ensconced in our own private world, and keep others out. Our games of deflation can include pretending that we don't care, that circumstances don't really matter or that we don't really count in life and are not important. Deflation may also include habitual patterns such as giving up personal opinions or preferences and falsely agreeing with all sides in an argument, 'going with the flow', introversion, social withdrawal into remoteness or isolation. It may include emotional collapse, passivity and passive resistance, apology and sulking. Or it may involve self-narcotization, numbing out to our emotions, emotional disconnection, or putting a lid on our emotions and 'keeping them under wraps' in a way that robs us of a huge amount of our energy.

When we habitually deflate we may even become fatalistic or feel like a victim of life and circumstance, we may incessantly blame ourselves for our own problems and feel that we have a 'character flaw' that we can do nothing about, that life is overwhelming and too much to bear, or we may just feel too tired to be bothered to engage fully with life.

Deflation leads to a muting of our emotions. Muting means turning down or subduing our natural emotional responses so we experience a toned down or stifled, version of what we are really feeling. We might swallow our emotions, choke them back, damp them down, smother or suppress them. We may energetically push and stuff our strong emotions back down inside our bodies; we may numb out, haze out or narcotize ourselves against our pain.

All of these deflationary themes allow us to suppress or contain emotions we do not want to face or feel. And all of these games, almost by definition, are associated with depression.

If you take a look back at the last three paragraphs you will notice that many of these strategies accurately describe some of the significant symptoms of depression! So when we rely on these types of games we are feeding our own potential to feel depressed, we are adding spin to the depression's downward spiral.

So, let's be very clear here: to be depressed we must employ some strategies of deflation; depression depends on it. And conversely if we habitually deflate in our strategic attempt to smother and dull the sharpness of uncomfortable emotions then some form of depression becomes likely - it is a natural result.

If we also use these two strategies of deflation and rigidity and habitually resist our emotions, then that can add into a depressive mix.

Let's explore how these games of deflation and rigidity can come about, the pain they can inadvertently cause and their links with depression.

Deflation and Muting Painful Emotions

One afternoon at school when I was in my teens, I headed towards my desk after lunch, unaware that a stout boy from a different grade was closely shadowing me. Out of nowhere a hard roundhouse punch landed on the side of my face and I stumbled sideways.

Testosterone fuelled shouts of, "Get him! Get him!" and "Fight! Fight!" went up, as the boys who had goaded my attacker into hitting me cheered him on. My shock almost instantly left, and I felt livid, saw red.

I regained my footing and spun to face my attacker. We squared up, started throwing punches at each other's heads. I felt restricted by the school blazer I was wearing, but he wore only a sweater over his shirt and could move more freely. I sensed my disadvantage, and when my next punch landed, as he reeled from the blow, I instantly followed through, moved in and unbalanced him with my leg. As he part-stumbled I grabbed hold of the back of his shirt collar and spun him further, then took a fist-hold on the back of his sweater with my other hand.

Before I knew what I was doing, I had pushed him hard and propelled him at speed headlong into an old-fashioned solid cast iron wall radiator. He fell backwards like a sack of cement; flat out, eyes open but only the whites visible. He seemed to have stopped breathing. I thought he was dead.

As I froze in fear, a panicked sequence of pictures raced through my mind: dead boy, principal, police, police station, door, cell, lock, key… key thrown away. For a moment I felt overwhelming dread, like I had just thrown my whole life away.

The boy gasp-spluttered a breath - he had only been temporarily knocked out. His eyes rolled back into place, and his friends gathered around, picked him up, and half-carried him out of the room.

I barely moved, held my breath. My classmates were silent as well - shocked, I think. Deep down I was terrified, but was too stunned to feel it, or too afraid to feel it, too scared to feel anything maybe. I choked the emotion back and stuffed the anger, the fear, the dread, the whole trauma, deep down inside my body, into my belly. In an instant, I squelched it all.

At that moment my English teacher walked breezily into the room and, having missed all the action, ordered everyone to their seats. "Good afternoon. Please take out your textbooks and turn to page…" She began teaching the lesson. Soon I felt blank, hazy and disconnected.

None of my friends mentioned the incident, checked if I was hurt or chivvied me on. For the rest of the afternoon I remained withdrawn, vacant and disassociated, unable to focus or take in any of the teaching. And I internally crystallized a mistake that I had in smaller measure made several previous time in life: I unconsciously equated the emotions of rage with the behaviors of attack and fighting. I now equated fighting with death. I consolidated my belief that anger and rage were dangerous feelings; that if I allowed rage to arise someone would get killed. From that point onwards I decided to control my rage by muting it, keeping it under wraps. Whenever any strong emotions were triggered in me I experienced a type of automatic, instantaneous shut down. Eventually, the shut down effect became pre-verbal, instinctive, and meant that I didn't ever feel the big emotions that were triggered in me.

If my anger or rage were triggered (and by this time it took a lot to trigger those emotions) you might see something strange: a redness would rise in my chest as the anger was provoked; it would creep up to my throat and seep into my lower cheeks… then some internal force would brace, resist and drag it back down inside. My cheeks would turn blotchy white, then would blanch completely and the flush could be seen, like a receding red tide, progressively moving back down my neck and into my chest, downward inside my body. All the while, my internal story - one that I was absolutely convinced was true - was that I felt relaxed, normal, calm, that nothing was a 'problem'. But I had literally lost the ability to feel anger, and instead instinctively and unknowingly pushed it, squashed it down into my belly.

Where it lay buried and festered for years.

Rigidity and Resisting Painful Emotions

From early childhood I learned that there were some emotions I was simply not allowed to feel or show. My mind goes back to an earlier preschool time, when I was about four years old.

During recess I was playing in the schoolyard when I noticed a child my age lift up a heavy, hinged iron drainage lid. Ever the do-gooder, I raced over in an attempt to save him from harm. I reached down to steady the lid, to stop him getting hurt, but as I did so he let go. The lid thumped back into its tight fitting frame, trapping and crushing my thumb. A nearby teacher rushed over and raised the metal lid.

I felt woozy with pain as I looked at my hand. My thumb was squashed, bloodied and was already turning blue-black underneath the thumbnail. I whimpered quietly as the teacher took me inside, phoned my parents and bandaged my thumb.

My father quickly collected me, carried me to his car and drove me to the doctor's office. Doctor Morris removed the bandage and took a look. He whispered to my father, "This is quite serious. His nail will have to come off - he might lose his thumb otherwise. I can do it now, that's the best."

Dad held me gently, cradling me in his arms and turning my head away from the activity. I can only imagine what he was feeling, knowing the pain his young son was in and what he was about to go through.

The doctor took my hand and began spraying a local anesthetic, ethyl chloride, on my thumb. It stung like crazy, and I struggled as the cold bit in and took effect, completely freezing my whole thumb tip. Dad held me more firmly as the doctor took a pair of pliers, gripped the offending nail and forcibly pulled it out of its bed.

Even with the anesthetic, the ripping hurt like hell. I kicked and screamed, but was held too tightly to escape. When it was over, the wound was quickly dressed and I cried big loud sobs as my father did his best to placate me, telling me I was safe, that it was all over.

"Let's go to Nannie's," Dad said, as he lifted me back into the car. "She'll make us a nice cup of tea. That will make you feel better." I loved my grandmother, and nodded in agreement.

Dad carried me into Nannie's house, careful to protect my damaged hand. Nannie saw the bandage and blurted out, "Oh my God! What has he done? Is he okay?"

"Yes, he's fine," Dad replied. "He hurt his thumb in school and had to go to the doctor's. He has had his nail taken off, but he was so brave… You know what? He didn't even cry! Can we have a cup of tea to make it all better?"

In my four-year-old body I felt uncomfortable, guilty, but I played along, staying mute to the deceit. I'd cried and kicked and screamed and yelled, but my father was lying about it. He was covering for me, pretending that I'd been 'a brave little soldier' when I must have been a coward. And my young mind got it: it must be so bad, so shameful, to be a baby, to cry when in pain, that we have to lie about it. We have to pretend to be brave; we have to pretend that we don't feel these horrible emotions.

I stood up, puffed up my chest and I 'toughed up'; I physically blocked my feelings of vulnerability and weakness, I willfully braced against the discomfort that remained and pretended that I was not hurting, that I was 'fine'.

Triggered into hurt, pain and, eventually, shame, I energetically resisted those emotions. I changed my internal story into one of, 'I'm tough, I can handle it,' and used my body to make the story seem real. I changed my physiology to support the appearance of being unhurt, like these events had no impact on me, could not reach or touch me.

The long-term effect was that I braced against my own deeper emotions, especially ones that involved fear, tenderness or exposure. I put on a façade of being okay, unruffled, unbothered, even when I was feeling scared or threatened. I toughened my body against my softer feelings, pretended that I was a 'man', not a wimp or girly. I adopted an air of 'got-it-all-together' in the emotions department, dishonestly pretending that I never felt vulnerable or scared.

The Price of Deflation and Rigidity

What I didn't know at the time of these events, of course, was that there would be a long-term price to pay for my habitual shutdowns and resistances.

Our bodies and minds cannot selectively suppress, cannot accurately identify a single emotion and subdue only it. Bracing against, smothering, swallowing or talking ourselves out of an emotion means we are in truth manipulating a whole host of emotions.

Because I began to suppress and swallow anger and rage, I muted a whole swathe of other big emotions in life. In fearfully muting anger and rage my ability to experience many other high-energy emotions was also automatically compromised, shut down. Soon I experienced less joy, less excitement, less light-heartedness. I felt less empowered, less confident, less all round positivity in my life. Instead I experienced compromised, middle ground feelings - such as indifference, disconnection, vagueness and numbness, general low-level unsettlement - but nothing vivid, nothing big, nothing sharp. My whole emotional experience became muted.

And when I braced against fear and vulnerability I also unintendedly steeled myself against many other deep emotions. I hardened myself and shut down to some emotions that I eventually yearned for, really longed to feel. I began to resist physical affection, to shun hugs, and I automatically blocked tenderness, empathy, closeness, connection and even love. Of course, I didn't consciously know I was doing these things, but the emotional results were lasting. Soon I began to feel isolated, separate, excluded in some inexplicable way from the heart of life - like I was an outsider looking in rather than an integral part of it. It began to feel as if something was missing in my life, but I had no idea what it was.

With both deflation and rigidity at play in my life as strategies of emotional avoidance it is no surprise that as I grew older my general emotional range became crimped, contained and narrow-band. I began to feel less and less. I had forced down my natural high-energy feelings and stuffed them deep into my gut. I had braced myself against my natural deep or sensitive feelings and blocked them out. And I had created a double whammy in my own life, a powerful bind of no ups and no downs. I felt straightjacketed, held firmly in a middle band of only 'moderate' emotions, controlled emotions, polite emotions - nothing too exciting, nothing too profound; nothing too energizing, nothing too scary. Every experience became mediocre, flat.

Life lost its color, its vivacity, its up-ness; it lost its depth, its authenticity and its meaning. I eventually seemed to become a ghost, wandering aimlessly in a grey wasteland of existence; unmoved by any circumstance, separated from the best and the worst, but trapped in a uniform, one-dimensional universe of my own creation. I felt rootless and unnourished: as if I was living a half-life, chewing cardboard. For years I lived a life in a band of stuckness, numbness, haziness, anxiety and resentment. It was a moderate form of depression.

Does any of this seem familiar? Your life experiences will undoubtedly be different from mine and yet, if you have experienced depression, they may well bear some similarities.

For depression to exist we must deflate, we must suppress, push down our emotions: depression is predicated on this pattern. We must shut down, stuff down or in some other way mute our natural instinctive feelings. We must control them and modify them by manipulating our bodies and our minds; using our beliefs to create stories that shift our in-the-moment emotional responses, and make this manipulation seem natural, normal or inevitable. We may also get emotionally rigid, and brace ourselves against emotions. And if we both deflate and get rigid we have a good recipe for fostering depression.

Instructions: How Do You Shut Down Your Emotions?

Download the audio and script at www.kevinbillett.org/book-bonus

Let's try another experiment to check out your habits. What strategy or strategies do you use to avoid your real feelings?

Intention:
That you discover how you shut down some specific emotions
Time:
10 to 12 minutes
Emotional level:
Mildly to moderately emotional
What you need:
Quiet space. Tissues
At the end:
Short break of 5 minutes or so

Let's go back to an old memory or two and find out how you automatically responded when you were emotionally triggered. This exercise is not designed to be intensely emotional; in fact you may feel only subtle feelings, and that is fine. It is an emotionally disassociated introspection, and it is designed to illustrate how you unconsciously avoid some emotions.

You could ask a friend or loved one to read out the next section to you, use the CD or get online and work with the audio version of this enquiry. You could also do it as an eyes-open/eyes-closed exercise on your own - it just takes a little longer that way. In any case, read it through to the end of the exercise first so you understand it, then do it!

Exercise 4: How do you shut down your emotions?

Find a quiet place, somewhere where you can just sit and be uninterrupted. Take a seat, make yourself comfortable, and relax. Now close your eyes, and take a good long deep breath in... and let it all the way out...

Imagine that you are sitting safely on a comfortable couch in a viewing room, with a large, blank video screen on the wall in front of you... one on which we are shortly going to ask some old memories to play out.

You can welcome a mentor - a being you know or one that is born from your imagination... a soul that is wise, and open and can give loving guidance... And you can welcome a guardian angel of grace and absolute safety if you wish... feeling its protective presence safely enveloping you... You can even ask the mentor to provide a clear crystal dome of protection, and to wrap you safely inside it... one that allows in only love and positivity... and keeps everything else on the outside... Good... So just rest in the knowledge that you are completely safe here...

Putting your attention on the screen now... you can bring the screen closer, or push it farther away... You can adjust the size of the screen, to make it bigger or smaller... and at any time you can alter the focus until it's either sharper or more fuzzy... You can adjust the color and brightness... You can even make it black and white if you like... So now, begin to make all these adjustments so that you begin to feel more relaxed and comfortable now... Great...

Notice the DVD player right below the screen... In your hand is a remote control device... and a DVD disc in its case... On this DVD is recorded some old scenes or memories related to a time when you were emotionally triggered and you shut down the feelings you may initially have had... You can rest in the knowledge that you are safe on this couch and in complete control of how this old scene plays out... You can even stop it at any time and move onto a less uncomfortable scene if you wish.

Now, as you remain seated on the couch, pick up the remote control... as you get ready to watch an old scene play out on the screen... Then give the mentor the case containing the DVD disc... and let the mentor put the DVD disc into the player... Great... You may not yet know what scene is going to play, and that is fine... You can simply watch from the safety of the couch and discover...

The first scene may be of a memory that caused you to deflate, to shrink or withdraw emotionally. Maybe it was a time when something triggered you and you muted or swallowed or choked back what you were really feeling... a time when something happened and triggered you into shutting down some emotion... Maybe something happened that felt like it was getting out of control... was too exciting, too energetic, too strong... Maybe it was time when you, or someone else, felt enraged or angry, and it scared you...

Maybe it was a time when emotions ran so high that you automatically put a lid on them and closed them down... Or maybe it was a time when something happened that scared or frightened you and you suppressed the feeling...

Now press the 'Play' button on the remote and just let the scene play out... as you sit safely watching the screen ... As you watch from a distance and see what unfolded... hear any words that were spoken... just get a sense of what emotion or emotions were triggered in you... What did you initially feel... even it was very subtle or fleeting?... What was that?...

Now, as the scene moves forward... how did you respond next?... How did you suppress the intensity of the feelings that were triggered?... How did you shut down, or subdue what you were really feeling?... What happened with your body?... And what story were you telling yourself... what was your inner dialogue?... And how did you eventually feel?... Was it a turned down, or muted feeling?... Okay...

Now press the pause button on the remote, and get ready to push the 'next chapter' button, the one that will take you to the next scene... still remembering that at all times you will remain safely on the couch, with the mentor and the guardian angel... behind the crystal dome... and safely in control of how the scene plays out...

And now press the 'next chapter' button, and get ready to press 'play' one more time... This time the DVD will reveal an old memory of a time when you were triggered in a different way... Maybe this time you felt hurt or embarrassed, or sad or lost... or some other deep-energy emotion... This may be a time when something happened... or someone said or did something that made you feel insecure or incompetent, or unloved... And this is a time when you blocked that feeling, resisted it... or in some way blew it off... This is a time when you steeled yourself against an uncomfortable emotion, hardened yourself against it...

So just press the 'play' button and let the scene unfold... Where and when is this?... Just watch as the memory reveals itself... Look as the action continues, and notice from a distance... Hear any words that were spoken... and just get a sense of what emotion or emotions were really triggered in you... What did you initially feel, even it was very subtle or fleeting?... What was that?...

And now, as the scene moves forward... how did you respond next?... How did you avoid the intensity of the feelings that were triggered?... How did you suppress or resist what you were really feeling?... How did you block it or brace against it... How did you shut down to it?... What happened with your body?... And what was your mind saying?... What dialogue was running internally?... And now get a sense of what you eventually felt... how did you eventually feel?... Good...

Now you can press the 'stop' button on your remote... and now the 'power off' button that shuts the screen down, makes it turn to blank... Let the old memories fade with it, and turn to grey...

Take a few seconds to come back to neutral... then thank your mentor and your guardian angel... And now allow the whole imagined room with the screen to disappear... And gently allow awareness to come back to the present moment... and the present place... Sitting where you are sitting right now...

Take a fresh, long, deep breath in... and let it all the way out... And you can softly open your eyes now, when you are ready.

Great job!

So what did you discover? Can you see that a part of your tendency, at least, is to deflate, to collapse and mute your strong emotions? Just stop for a moment and consider: Are there other times when you have reacted similarly with this type of suppression? Has deflation, emotional collapse and smothering your feelings, become a habit in your life? And have you also played games of resistance with your emotions by blocking or resisting them?

If so, then congratulations, because you have uncovered a significant link with the condition of depression - and this realization will serve you well when we come to the clear out exercises, the Journey process work introduced in chapter 9.

But before we get to the process work that allows us to completely free ourselves from the limitations of our old habits, let us take a deeper look at an area that naturally feeds and sustains these patterns of avoidance - our beliefs and our vows.

CHAPTER 5

The Fuel of Negative Personal Story:

Disempowering Beliefs and Vows

Disempowering Beliefs Shape Our Personal Story

So what shapes our personal story? If we have regular inner dialogue that encourages emotional collapse or shutdown, what causes us to run this dialogue? And why does it seem so compelling, so real?

We are fundamentally influenced from the earliest of ages - perhaps even in the womb - by the people we are related to and closest to. Like sponges we absorb the beliefs of those around us. And some of that influence is disempowering or even downright negative.

Despite probable good intentions, our parents, siblings, close relatives, friends, teachers and authority figures pass on their own negative conditioning to us. We pick up on, and are imprinted by, their believed limitations, restrictions and negativities, many of which they too have simply inherited. We learn these beliefs through listening to others' words and by observing their actions, and empathizing or identifying with them. And often we are rewarded or punished according to our compliance, or lack of it, to authority's will.

These beliefs shape a core part of our internal 'map' of reality; they help create our sense of what is true or real and what is not. They shape our perceptions of ourselves and of our place in the world. And, however we have built them, our belief systems around emotions and emotionality are a key to understanding, and ultimately, to freeing ourselves from depression.

You may have heard your mother say, "Oh, come along dear, don't make such a fuss! Stop that crying and just get on with things"; or your father saying, "Stop those tears or I'll give you something to cry about!" Or you may have seen a parent bite back on their own tears, or close down their own emotions, and have learned by watching them that it is not okay to cry, to feel, or to show emotions.

You may have heard a friend say, "Stop being such a wimp!" or "Get over it!" or a teacher saying, "Toughen up!" and come to believe that feeling emotions is a weakness that shames you or compromises your ability to survive and thrive.

What we are really hearing is a reflection of other people's conditioned beliefs and fears about emotions and feeling. However we learned them, these beliefs about the inappropriateness or 'badness' of feeling our emotions become part of our perceived reality and perpetuate an internal 'story' about our emotions.

We also generate our own disempowering beliefs about emotions when we experience the dramas and traumas of life and mistake the feelings associated with the circumstance for the threat or the danger of the circumstance itself - exactly as I did when I went through the experiences with my thumbnail, with Debs in the buggy, and with the school fight, and came to internally fear the feelings associated with the actions in those memories. Those events created strong disempowering beliefs that shaped and fuelled my internal story about the necessity of avoiding strong emotions.

Then, in adult life, we may find that an internal dialogue automatically arises in conjunction with any strong emotion. The emotion and the story arise simultaneously, and often we can barely tell them apart. Then we talk ourselves out of our intense feelings with, "Can't go there" "Got to snap out of that one" or "Shape up, it's not that bad" or "I'll show them how tough I really am", and so on. We add story, an internal commentary, to our emotions and, as we have seen already, our emotions get suppressed, diffused and turn into pervasive moods.

Even our deeply distressing stories about emotions, like, "This always happens to me! Why me?" or, "I'm a victim here, and there's nothing I can do about it", are stories that allow us to take the sharpness or sting out of an emotion and moderate it, turn it down. But as a by-product, the story turns that emotion into a general mood. And as we continue to feed our moods with more stories, our moods turn into states; and finally we have unconsciously created a vital component of depression.

Alongside these negative stories we can also be holding on to another type of hook that can bind into and reinforce our negative or compromising beliefs: limiting vows and promises.

Think back to the story I related at the beginning of this book about the accident I had with my little sister. At the most of my greatest terror I blurted out to God the desperate offer of a deal: "Dear God… please let her be alive! If you do, I promise I will never do that again." I had made a classic vow, an 'if-then' promise, and I was on the hook to God, for life. From then on, because it was a matter of life and death, I could never do that again - could never let go, never be free and easy, silly, childlike and carefree.

The power, the sheer hold of the vow was immense. It shaped and fuelled the belief that all these fun behaviors were dangerous. It meant that, as well as believing that I had to instantly grow up and 'be responsible', there was no other possible option; it was that or death. The vow interacted with a belief and turned it into a certainty.

I've explored many areas of my life and found that old, inappropriate vows were still in play - some from childhood, some from adulthood. I discovered, for example, vows of parental compliance and vows to be 'good' that restricted me to old childish perceptions about how I should be and behave in life. I discovered strong promises to always 'work hard' and study intently for school tests that, even in later life, seemed to undermine my enjoyment of free time and recreation. And I discovered that when I got married to my previous wife and made vows of fidelity and loyalty, 'till death us do part' their effect was in play years after our divorce, when I still felt responsible to and for her, even though we were both in new, committed relationships.

For the past 17 years I've been exploring with my seminar groups the insidious grip of old vows, and been shocked to find out how common they are, and how pervasive their hold can become. I've been told about vows of emotional closure, vows of retribution, vows of commitments and prohibitions; I've even heard of 'death vows' where, because of 'survivor guilt' or a feeling of deep undeserving a person commits or promises to die by a particular age in life.

Some vows seem healthy at the time we make them, seem like a good commitment to make, but then maybe our circumstances change and they become outmoded and unhelpful. Some vows are unhealthy from the time we make them; maybe they were made under duress, or in a moment of panic (like mine with Debs), and those vows begin to mess with us emotionally from the time we first utter the words.

However they are made, these vows all have something in common: they powerfully compromise our abilities to feel, to behave and to be as we currently would choose in life. They bind us compellingly to an old consciousness and they cause us pain and distress long after they're made. We need to find a way to let go of them, clear them if we are to be free from this bind.

The good news about vows is that they can be changed in the same way as beliefs: by deconditioning them from our bodies and beings before reconditioning ourselves with fresh commitments to being open, free and empowered to make healthy and supportive choices in any moment in life.

It's time to release some of this pent-up old conditioning. So let's explore with a guided introspection that is designed to clear out a combination of old issues: it will help us release some fears about feeling emotions and it will help us change some old disempowering beliefs and vows and make them more positive and supportive.

Exercise 5

Instructions: Releasing Fears, Changing Beliefs And Vows

Download the audio and script at www.kevinbillett.org/book-bonus

This exercise, like the one in the last chapter, is not designed to be intensely emotional; in fact you may feel only subtle or moderate feelings, and that is fine. It is mostly an emotionally disassociated introspection, and it is designed to change the way we feel and react to an old memory or circumstance, and to change some disempowering beliefs and vows that arose from that memory. In parts the exercise is humorous, very silly in fact, so let go and have fun with it. It should take about 45 or 50 minutes, so make sure to allow sufficient time to undergo the exercise thoroughly.

You could ask a friend or loved one to read out the exercise to you, or you can access the online audio version, which comes with some extra benefits. But for this exercise, you cannot just read it to yourself - your eyes need to be closed for the whole thing. So, whichever way you work, first read the script through to the end of the exercise so you understand it, then do it!

Instructions for the person reading the script to you are included in parentheses [like this]. Wherever there are three dots, like this '...' the reader should pause for a moment. Read at a relatively brisk pace.

Find a quiet place, somewhere where can just sit and be uninterrupted - turn phones off, make sure you have some private space and time. Take a seat, and find a nice comfortable position, relax and close your eyes.

Intention:
That you change your relationship with some old fears and begin to change some unhealthy or unsupportive beliefs and promises from the past
Time:
45 to 50 minutes
Emotional level:
Mildly to moderately emotional
What you need:
Quiet space. Pen and paper. Tissues
At the end:
Short break of 15 minutes or so

Exercise 5: Releasing fears, changing beliefs and vows

As you relax and settle, just close your eyes... and turn your awareness inwards... Now imagine that you are sitting safely on a comfortable couch in a viewing room, with a large, blank video screen on the wall in front of you... You can welcome a mentor, a wise sage or saint... someone who is profoundly free in their being... and a guardian angel if you wish... feeling its protective presence safely enveloping you... You can even ask the mentor to provide a crystal dome of protection... One that allows in only love and positivity... and keeps everything else on the outside... Good... Just rest in the knowledge that you are completely safe here.

*Putting your attention on the screen now... You can bring the screen closer, or push it farther away... You can adjust the size of the screen, to make it bigger or smaller ... and at any time you can alter the focus until it's either sharper or more fuzzy... You can adjust the color and brightness... You can even make it black and white if you like... So now, begin to make all these adjustments so that you **begin to feel more relaxed and comfortable now**... Great.*

*Now notice the DVD player right below the screen... and in your hand is a remote control device... and a DVD disc in its case... On this DVD is recorded an old scene or memory related to a fearful reaction you may have had in the past to a strong emotion or emotions... maybe one of your core avoidance emotions... one that, in the past, you might have avoided at all costs... It is a memory that long ago may have caused you to shut down, collapse... freeze... block... resist... or avoid a specific emotion or emotions... And you can rest in the knowledge that **you** are in complete control of how this old scene plays out.*

And now, as you remain seated on the couch, pick up the remote control... as you get ready to watch the old scene play on the screen... give the mentor the case containing the DVD disc... and let the mentor put the DVD disc into the player... Please nod your head to let me know when the disc has been inserted... [Give time]... Great.

*And now **press the 'Play' button on the remote and just let the scene play out from beginning to end**... as you sit safely watching the screen... And just let me know when the scene has completely played out... [Give time]... Great... So would you please briefly describe the scene to me?... [Let yourself describe it]... Thank you... And just for extra clarity, would you please tell me which specific emotions you may have blocked or shut down or avoided at that time?... [Let yourself answer]... Great, thank you.*

So, now put your attention back on the scene of that old memory on the screen... and just **push the 'Fast Play' button and let it play out really quickly right to the end...** And when it's finished you can let me know by giving a nod... [Give time]... That's great.

And **now press 'Fast Reverse'** and **see and hear** the scene running backwards... Now run the scene forwards again, triple speed... Now backwards triple speed, **seeing** everyone moving in reverse, **hearing** the words backwards... Now forwards again... Now backwards... Faster and faster each time... Forwards, backwards, forwards, back- wards... again and again... faster and faster ... Forwards, backwards, forwards, back- wards... until the scene and the words are a complete blur... And when everything is a complete blur, you can just nod your head to let me know... [Give time]... Excellent!

Now, give everyone in the scene, yourself included, silly fancy dress or cartoon charac- ters' outfits with funny ears and noses. Make all the scenery and props out of rubber or sponge or candy... Make it bouncy, or springy, and fun... And let everyone speak with very silly cartoon voices, or like they've been inhaling helium... You too!... Great!... Now add some funny cartoon-type music... and just watch and hear the scene play out with these silly costumes, the silly scenery, the silly voices and the silly music. **Notice how different it looks, sounds and feels** as the scene plays out to the end... Then run the scene backwards and forwards... faster and faster in each direction... seeing the ac- tions, hearing the words... especially as they are spoken backwards... faster and faster in each direction... incredibly fast ... and even faster still... until it's all a complete blur ... And when it's finished, just nod your head to let me know... [Join in the fun, and play! Give time]... Fabulous!

Now let the younger you in the scene step down off the screen and come over to join the you on the couch... And ask either the younger you in the scene or the mentor... What unhealthy beliefs... and vows or promises were formed here?... What unsupportive be- liefs about strong emotions did you form?... And what vows or promises of closure, shut down or collapse... or avoidance or distraction did you make?... How did you contrive to avoid such feelings and such circumstances in the future?... What did you decide?... Allow all the old beliefs, vows and promises to reveal themselves... and speak out all the words associated with each of them... [Let yourself answer. (The partner can help if nec- essary by repeating this paragraph.) Make sure you speak out loud the words associated with the beliefs, vows and promises. Write them all down so you can repeat them back later. Take time and make sure you empty out the old beliefs.]

So now turn to the person or people in the scene on the screen, and let them know that you understand that all these conditioned responses were born from a mistake... and probably from old conditioning that they had themselves absorbed earlier in their own lives... In your own words, please let them know that it is no longer appropriate to have that old stuff in place... [Give time] ... And tell them that it is your intention to let go of the old conditioning and replace it with new, empowering choices... and healthy truths, born from freedom... [Give time]... Good.

Now, turn to the mentor and ask that the old beliefs, vows and promises all be swept clean, be completely cleared out from every cell of your being... [Read out the list of beliefs, vows and promises you wrote down earlier]... Just let the mentor sweep, wash, hose, vacuum away every vestige of those old restrictive patterns... and you just **watch and feel as it all is cleared from every cell in your body** ... right down to the level of your DNA... and the genes in your DNA... refreshing and clearing... from every molecule of your being... from the spaces between the molecules... right down to the level of consciousness itself... making sure the mentor gets in to all the stuck places... all the dark corners ... all the secret places... until they are all completely cleared out... Take as much time as you need... [Give as much time as needed]... Please let me know by nodding your head when that is completely finished ... Fabulous!

And now turn again to the mentor, and ask for assistance in the formulation of new, wholesome, empowering realizations or deepest truths... new, empowering, freeing vows and decisions... **ones that are positively phrased, using only positive language and words**... ones that will allow you to remain open, fully connected in life and fulfilled... free to be your true self... And when you are ready, you can let me know what the new, healthy truths and decisions are... [Let yourself answer (the partner can give assistance if needed). Write down new realizations, truths, vows and decisions]... That's beautiful... Thank you... So now, as you repeat these realizations out loud, affirming their truth... [Read new truths and vows one by one, getting partner to repeat each one after you]

Just ask the mentor to install them all, to re-program them into every cell of the being... Ask the mentor to flood every particle of your being with these new, empowering certainties and decisions... making them an integral part of you... freeing you... revitalizing you... energizing you... letting you come to peace and completion... Allowing you to freely feel and experience all that life has to offer... [Give time]... Just let me know when this is absolutely complete... [Give sufficient time]... Wonderful.

And now, imagine opening your chest and your heart... and send forgiveness to the people associated with the old conditioning... forgiveness for anything that might need forgiving... And you can just whisper out that forgiveness... Great... And staying wide open, receive forgiveness from them for anything that might need forgiving in you...

however small or insignificant that might be... And finally forgive yourself for anything, and everything, that could use some forgiveness... [Give time]

And now, ask the younger you or the mentor what emotional resources or qualities **would** have helped at that time... **What emotional resources or qualities would have been needed for this scene to have played out much more positively and beneficially then?** ... What would have helped the younger you handle things much more healthily and supportively back then?

[Partner, be helpful. Get creative. Suggest qualities and ask if they would help: ability to stay open, ability and willingness to feel fully, courage, confidence, love, self-esteem, ability to open and speak from the heart, ability to speak the truth, realization of authentic self, etc.]

Now hand the younger you from the scene a big colorful bunch of balloons, with each balloon containing one of these resources... Let the younger you **breathe** into each of these balloon qualities, one by one, and feel the resources permeating the younger you. [Name each resource and allow it to be breathed in]

And now **watch** as the younger you with the big balloon bouquet climbs back up on the screen... and **see and hear and feel how differently it would have happened** with these new truths and decisions already installed... with full access to these new healthy resources and realizations... Let the scene play out, and **notice how things have changed now**... Notice how you are able to remain open and let emotions simply flow through your body now... with the full knowledge that any emotion fully felt takes you right into the heart of freedom... leaves you in clarity and at choice... living and acting from freedom now... fully able to embrace and welcome whatever arises... and respond healthily, authentically, positively now... And when the new scene has finished completely, you can let me know... Great... So what happened? How was it different this time?... How does that feel?... [Let yourself answer]... Fabulous!

And now, just allow the new, more resourceful younger you to come down off the screen, come over to you on the couch and hug and merge with you... letting the younger you grow up inside the body of the present you... allowing any other similar memories relating to this issue to arise ... and you can see the memories as they arise ... or you can get a sense or knowing that this is happening ... **and as each memory arises, let it be washed through by the consciousness of the new resources and freedom inside you**... with the growing realization and awareness that you are open, feeling, fully engaged in life and completely free... **Let each memory be energetically transformed** *by the new qualities*... *Great*... *And you can take as much time as is needed for this to happen... [Give sufficient time]... And just nod your head when it is complete, and you've arrived at the present moment... Excellent... So what took place? [Let yourself answer]*

And now seeing and hearing and feeling what it is like to be finally and completely free from that old pattern... open, fully alive, vibrant now ... you can thank the mentor, and the guardian angel if you had one, and you may leave the viewing room, walking out happy in the experience of your new freedom, confidence and wholeness... Great!

Now, imagine stepping in to the future a day from now... Get a sense of how you are feeling... of what has improved in your life over the last 24 hours... How do you feel?... [Let yourself answer]... Great... And now step in to the future a week from now... Just check what shifts have already taken place... Get a sense in your body of how your confidence and trust have deepened... Can you feel the changes?... Great...

What else has changed?... [Let yourself answer]... Great...

And step in to the future a month from now... What about that old emotion, or those emotions, you were previously afraid to feel?... How easy is it to allow that now?... How healthy and free do you feel one month from now?... [Let yourself answer]... Great... And now just step into the future six months from now... getting a full sense of how your life has opened, and improved... How you have changed, deepened and grown six months from now?... See, and hear and feel how amazing it is to be you... Notice all the things that are newly possible in life... How good is it to be you, fully engaged in life, in this body, at this time... [Let yourself answer]... Wonderful!

And now step one whole year into the future... and open fully to the new experience of life that is being lived... What does it feel like when you are truly open to the full experience of life?... What differences show up in the experience of life, now that you are able and willing to allow all emotions to come and play... and dance through you... and take their leave?... How has life deepened, become more profound in this new awareness?... And how has it lifted, lighted and become more effortless... more joyous... more engaging... and more fun?... [Let yourself answer]... Excellent.

And knowing that time is just an illusion, and that everything that can be brought into consciousness is already here in consciousness... in the present moment... right here, right now... just come back to the present moment basking and celebrating in the extraordinary freedom of your deepest self...

And knowing that you will only be able to open your eyes as soon as all parts of you are fully integrated and agreed that this transformation can only deepen and grow over time, that this realization of freedom and openness can only flourish and expand, and that your deepest authenticity can only unfold and express itself healthily and wholesomely in all ways, and when all parts of you are fully integrated and agreed that this can happen perfectly, automatically, of its own accord, effortlessly and organically, you may open your eyes now, when you are ready.

Great job! Congratulations!

Give yourself at least a short break before continuing your reading. It may take a while for the results of this exercise to integrate, so if you need to put the book down and come back to it later, please do so. In any case, stay open and allow the results of the exercise to filter through, until it is complete.

You should now feel at least a little more relaxed and free in relation to that old memory and beliefs and vows that may have arisen out of it. And, if you wish, you can repeat this exercise as many times as you want - working with the same memory of emotional shutdown, or with other different memories. The more you use the exercise the stronger the results will be.

And now it is time to move on. In the next section I'll share some of my personal experiences of emotional openness, something that has taken me years to really understand. It's a crucial step in truly feeling our emotions and understanding that it is safe and healthy to do so.

CHAPTER 6

The Only Way Out is In and Through

Let me tell you another story - one that begins to reveal the path you will need to follow to experience the freedom I spoke of at the beginning of this book.

Like for many people, my high school years were difficult ones. My early experience with the thumbnail had made me somewhat falsely chipper, stalwart and protected - a little covered emotionally. I was scared to let people see beneath my guard in case they discovered that I was really weak and vulnerable. My experience with Debs and the baby buggy had made me not only serious and contained but anxious about getting things wrong, nervous about upsetting people and being judged and found wanting. And my traumatizing fight had caused me to fear anger - my own and others' - and led to a more comprehensive shutdown, not just of anger and rage, but of most high-energy emotions.

I experienced all the normal adolescent worries: about self confidence, looks, sexual confidence, intelligence, and the 'cool' factor. I travelled a distance to school, lived separately from my school friends and struggled to belong, to feel included. I was subjected to sometimes severe, random bullying by gangs. And after the long bus ride each day, I often came home to an empty house and felt lonely and un-cared-for. I felt rootless, confused and stressed, and I was barely coping with life.

I fell in love with a girl who had her own insecurities, a difficult home life, and a tendency towards dramatic emotional explosions and shutdowns. Though we were attracted to, and protective of each other, neither of us was emotionally healthy enough to provide anything like adequate support. After some months my girlfriend took an overdose of painkillers. Although she survived physically unharmed, I took it as a personal failure, a shortcoming that I had no antidote to.

By 16 I felt as if I was sleepwalking through life. My parents noticed that I was withdrawn, unusually quiet and seemed 'down'. My mother took me to see a psychiatrist, and for the first time I was diagnosed with depression. The doctor prescribed pills, and I took them for a few weeks before deciding that they didn't help. I stopped taking them without telling anyone.

I struggled on for a few months until something unexpected and cataclysmically life-altering happened. It freed me from the all-pervasive lid I had put over my life, and its positive effect lasted for several years.

That day I came home from school to an empty house and flopped into an armchair. As usual, I was stewing over my burdensome problems - problems I had no answers to. I felt empty. Everything felt pointless, and I was just too tired to fight that feeling. So I stopped resisting. For a moment I stopped my internal dialogue of struggle and victimhood, and surrendered. I simply let the feeling of pointlessness be present and felt.

It grew until I felt flooded with the feeling of pointlessness. School, relationships, home life, life itself - it all felt overwhelmingly pointless. Not having the energy to do anything about it, I sat with it, felt the weight and the enormity of it.

Spontaneously, I started to experience even deeper emotions. It was as if there were layers of emotions and shortly after one layer was exposed and felt it deepened and turned into a different one. Within a few minutes the feeling of pointlessness turned into one of hopelessness. I sat still and just noticed and felt. The hopelessness grew, and become pervasive. Soon it seemed as if everything was hopeless: I was hopeless, humanity was hopeless, the whole of existence hopeless.

I continued to sit still, and again the feeling changed again. I began to feel pure overwhelm, and it kept getting bigger. It seemed endless, as if it was absolutely everywhere, filling every crack and space in the universe. I feared it would suffocate me, take me down and obliterate me, but I had no will left to move away from it. So I stayed still, noticed and felt.

The overwhelm turned into devastation. Devastation was at the core of everything, as if all reality was appearing inside it. It felt as if devastation was destroying the fabric of that reality, as if it were tearing apart the whole universe and everything in it, including me. I silently let go into the destruction.

I felt a quick flush of fear as everything turned into blackness. It was pure, complete, all absorbing. The blackness became empty, and void-like. It felt like the end, like death. I surrendered.

After a few minutes I became aware that the blackness, the void, was shifting, that it was beginning to get lighter. I felt a new energy come into it, as if it were vibrating at a high frequency in its core. The vibration increased in frequency, became scintillating and sparkling, like all-immersing champagne bubbles. It was joyous and elevating. It was almost surreally uplifting, ecstatic.

The feeling was expansive, everywhere: there was no sense of 'me' experiencing it, just the fullness of the experience itself. It was as if the uplifting energy had subsumed my sense of 'me', and turned everything into pure, open presence.

Although I had no idea at that time what had just happened to me, I had suddenly and fortuitously deepened through some emotional layers and had opened into my core, my own essence. And at the epicenter of my being was expansiveness, freedom, light. Having really opened and surrendered with my emotions, I had found that they led directly into my soul, into what is always free.

Abruptly, I opened my eyes. I stood, shook myself off and went into the kitchen to get something to eat. I forgot about the experience, gave it no significance or weight. But without my attention or my noticing it, something significant had shifted in my life.

Within a short time I broke up with my girlfriend, settled more easily into my schoolwork, reconnected with some old friends and started socializing with a different, more positive crowd. I seemed to be more in agreement and natural alignment with my parents: for the first time in many years I felt that they really loved me, cared about me and wanted the best for me. I felt loved by them, and I felt love for them. Within months I had found a beautiful and emotionally healthy new girlfriend, and fell headlong in love. My outlook changed, became more optimistic. I became more confident, more robust and outward going. I was more active, more sporting, and more sociable. I became, essentially, happy.

As I look back I see very clearly what I was unaware of at the time: after my experience of surrendering emotionally and opening into the core of my being I felt the best about myself that I had ever felt, more alive and full of life than I had felt since I was a seven-year-old child. Turning, facing, and emotionally opening to what I had previously worried about, avoided, wrestled and wrangled with, and then staying with those emotions until they turned into the light in the core of my being, led directly to almost a decade of healthy positive living.

It didn't completely and permanently solve my issue with depression - I needed to learn some more lessons and make some more discoveries before that absolute turnaround happened. But it was a huge pointer, a massive revelation. If only I'd known it at the time!

Freedom Comes Through Feeling Your Emotions Fully

If we open into the core of any emotion - no matter how strong or scary that emotion might be - and let it burn right through, we will open into source, the expansive essence of our being. Even school kids can do it.

A number of years ago in South Africa, a school that we visited had a bullying and fighting problem. Tempers would flare and scraps would regularly break out among the eight- to ten-year-old children. Brandon suggested that it might be good to teach the kids to feel anger. It sounds counterproductive, but it worked!

She got a trained teacher to do some exercises with the kids. They went out to the schoolyard and lined up. They stood and closed their eyes, clenched their fists and tensed their bodies, and went back in their minds to a time when they were angry or enraged. Then they were asked to welcome the anger, to bring it on with a vengeance, and to let go of the old memory, the old images. They were asked to feel it all, no matter how intense it got. They were not allowed to yell it out and disperse it, they were not allowed to move from the spot; they were just asked to stand and fully feel.

And they did a great job. Anger turned into rage, you could tell by the puffed up cheeks and reddened faces. Bodies became stiffer, looked like they were about to explode and still the kids were encouraged to bring it on, to turn it up and keep turning it up inside.

Then one by one their bodies softened as something released, let go. Looks of rage turned into smiles, then giggling, then full-on laughter. It looked like they broke through something, as if their struggles with their emotions lifted and they opened into something lighter, freer.

Eyes opened, and kids who some minutes ago felt like enemies rushed to each other, put their arms around each others shoulders and walked away happy, relaxed, the best of friends. They had learned to fully feel an emotion - in this case, anger or rage - rather than 'acting it out' with the behaviour of aggression. Afterwards the bullying and fighting in the school subsided; it fell almost completely away.

Let me be clear: this type of emotional opening is very different from the cathartic techniques used in some therapies. Therapeutic catharsis happens when you yell, lash out and hit pillows or other safe inanimate objects. Catharsis is where you blame and shout in role-play until there's nothing left. And while this type of action can definitely lead to release and feeling better, it does not in my experience lead to long-lasting results.

By opening silently, in stillness, and allowing our emotions to arise and be fully welcomed, something different happens. Though the sensations can sometimes feel incredibly intense, though they can seem to implode and explode simultaneously inside us, when we surrender to whatever feeling arises, it burns through and leaves nothing but pure energy in its wake. This same principle applies to any emotion fully welcomed and felt until it naturally subsides. The experience is liberating - and lasting.

By openly feeling - at least from time to time - we can gain another benefit. We may already understand in our minds that emotions are just emotions - neither good nor bad. We may already understand intellectually that our feelings are different from our behaviors. We can mentally grasp the knowledge that it is safe, even beneficial, to feel anything that arises, but it is only when we experience the results of emotional opening that our bodies finally get, at a cellular level, that it is okay to feel, that it is truly safe and healthy to be emotionally alive.

Timing is Everything: A Healthier Way to Feel Emotions

So should we always show our vulnerability, grief, rage or fear in public, no matter what? No, of course not.

Before we are carried away into falsely believing that to be free from depression we need to wear our hearts on our sleeves, open delicately like a flower all the time, or 'cathart' robustly like an opera diva throughout life, let me state clearly that we do not necessarily have to show vulnerability or rage or fear in public. We do not need to emote or be emotionally transparent in socially challenging situations. There are healthier, more practical options.

Let me give you an example. I was recently sitting at a dinner party table laden with delicious food and in the company of dear friends, when someone on the other side of the table made a comment that stuck in my craw and triggered me. I was aware that I was really angry. I'm sure that my face began to turn red as the anger flared into outrage. I caught myself and closed my eyes for two seconds, aware that I was in a social setting, with people I cared about, and that opening fully into anger and outrage might not be the most acceptable thing to do at a dinner table.

Years ago that would have been the end of a very short story. I would have squashed back the emotion I felt and pretended nothing had bothered me. I would have deflated and muted my anger at what my fellow diner had said. Instead of doing that I silently asked my body for a favor. Internally, I said to myself, "I know that you are really pissed off right now, and it's allowed." Then I imagined speaking directly to my body, asking, "Would you please let me take a rain check on feeling this emotion. If I promise to open and feel this rage until it is complete in the near future, would you please let me be emotionally neutral or even positive so I can be sociable and continue to chat normally for a while?"

The rage wafted away almost instantly, effortlessly dissipating, and I was left feeling quite normal.

I socialized calmly and naturally at the table until we finished the meal, and the group left for coffee in a different room, maybe 30 minutes after the triggering event. And then I could let myself feel what had been sparked off earlier.

I excused myself and headed to the bathroom. I locked the door, sat in silence on the bathtub's edge, and closed my eyes.

"Okay," I silently enquired, "What really happened just then? What were you really feeling?"

My mind flashed back to the incident, to the words I had heard spoken, and again I felt the full flush of anger. This time I welcomed it, opened with it. It quickly inflated, burgeoned into outrage. "How dare you!" I heard myself begin to internally scream. Then I stopped the story, just invited the internal pictures and words to drop, and got more honest.

"What were you really feeling in that moment?" I enquired. "What is here at the deepest level? What really wants to be felt?"

In seconds the rage burned through, and I felt like I had deepened into a completely different sensation. The feeling of marginalization arose, like I had been dismissed or pushed aside; it was subtle for a few moments, then it grew and became potent. I remained open and willing.

"What is next?" I asked silently. "What else wants to be felt?"

Marginalization turned into a feeling of insignificance that grew and burned with a power that felt like it could consume me. I surrendered into it. It lightened in energy, became very high frequency and turned into a vast light that seemed to include everything. I relaxed further and felt a deep wellbeing, sensed that everything was perfect, as it should be.

I gently opened my eyes, washed my face, and returned to the group, happy and at complete ease as we drank coffee and sang songs.

Emotional openness is a choice. It does not require you to do anything embarrassing or unusual in public. If you open and completely feel a strong emotion only once, allowing it to play out, story-free, to its natural conclusion, then your body, your whole being, will get it that that emotion no longer controls you. You will know at the deepest level that the emotion is free to come and go as it chooses in future, and you will know that it does not own you, no longer defines or drives you. And your painful, depression-catalyzing games of avoidance around this emotion will naturally fall away of their own accord.

For some of us it can take a little practice to relax, open and feel; it took me a while all those years ago. Happily, there are techniques that can help and methods that can make it safe and simple to feel your emotions and pass through them to openness. You will learn some of those techniques in chapter 9.

There are a couple more negative forces that can contribute to depression and its intensity. We will explore these two forces in the next chapter. Then it will be time for our main clearing work: the powerful guided introspections that are the core 'How To' section of this book. Here we will gently but powerfully directly experience the same type of work that completely freed me from depression and has kept me depression-free for more than 20 years.

CHAPTER 7

Two Negative Forces That Contribute to Depression

There are two additional negative forces that can contribute to depression and its intensity. Although neither of these forces is absolutely necessary as a prime cause of depression, each can add potently, heavily to the weight of pre-existing depression or can trigger a latent (or mild) depression and make it worse.

The first force is called the 'Expectation Gap'. This is the difference between our conscious or unconscious expectations about life, and the way our lives actually play out. It is the contrast between our ideals and our reality.

The second force is called 'Coping Strategy Overload'. This occurs when our normal coping mechanisms become overwhelmed and incapacitated, leading us into increased shutdown and pain.

Let's spend some time exploring these.

Negative Force #1: The Expectation Gap

Widespread depression is a modern and growing phenomenon. But it was not always this way; past generations seemed to respond differently to life's challenges.

My paternal grandparents, Nannie and Gramps, for example, were both great storytellers. They were wonderful at painting vivid, action-packed, emotionally charged pictures of what life had been like when they were young.

They were born in the early years of the 20th century into poor, proud, hard-working families. My grandfather was a deep-seam coalminer, and my grandmother, while keeping their house spotlessly clean, took in laundry to add to their income. For most of their lives they earned very little and by modern British standards were genuinely poor. In their earlier lives they lived in cramped, cold accommodations, often went hungry, could afford few indulgences, travelled little except for walking, and had holes in their clothes that would get darned and re-darned.

They lived through the General Strike during the 1920s, and other times when no income came into the house. Despite their desperate will to work, sometimes there was none, and there was little or no 'dole', no state or union pay-outs. Nannie recalled times when she had to 'run up a slate' with the local grocer, buying food on credit so they had something to eat. Gramps recalled scavenging on the tips, the vast pyramidal dumps of shale and underground waste that dominated the local hillsides, to find small pieces of coal to build their home fires.

They lived through the 1930s when economies around the world imploded and work became even scarcer and bellies even emptier. And through the tumult and traumas of the Second World War, enduring the draft and death of loved ones, bombs, rations, blackouts and the constant threat of invasion by a foreign army.

Yet the only stories I remember them telling about these hard times were positive and uplifting ones. They continually regaled me with tales of improvisation and making do, of family bonding and community support, of derring-do and escapades. They entertained and enthralled me to such an extent that when I was young I came to believe that I had truly missed out by being born too late to live through those times!

Far from being depressed about their circumstances, they responded healthily, it seemed. They did the best they could, they survived and were grateful, they enjoyed the ride, and they loved each other until they died.

Depression, it seems, was not such a common condition pre-Second World War. Indeed, various published research has indicated that depression is now at least 20 times more common than it was 50 years ago, and has reached almost epidemic proportions. And during that same period the use of prescribed anti-depressant medication has soared correspondingly, and suicide rates have risen massively.

Deprivation Does Not Create Depression

Depression is definitely a common and growing problem. But is it equally spread around the world; is it a uniform pattern? It seems not. This lesson was brought home to me in another way, on another continent.

I was in New Delhi, India, speaking with a friend, Ravi, when our topic turned to poverty in India. "There are levels of poverty, you see," he said, "What you see at the roadside, with the beggars and the disabled, is not real poverty. These people put on acts for the tourists; they are relatively well off. Would you like to see what real poverty looks like?"

I was taken aback, shocked at his suggestion that when I saw people dressed in rags and living in corrugated shelters under bridges and by the roadside, children barely into their teens or even younger carrying babies, and people with horrible physical disabilities begging at my car window, I had not been looking at 'real poverty'.

"Sure," I said, with trepidation in my voice. "I think I would like to see that." And we drove off in his rickety car, and into the insane traffic of New Delhi.

We drove through a maze of roads filled with trucks, cars, scooters, bicycles, people, dogs and cows. We wove our way through crowded side streets and dusty, trash-strewn paths, and eventually came to a huge garbage dump. It was covered with plastic bags, and food remains and filth. We got out of the car and explored. The whole place stank of rottenness and toxicity.

In the distance, I saw people and some flimsy shelters made from sticks and polythene sheeting. As we approached them I noticed several women squatting. They had what looked like old food cans in their hands and were scooping close to the ground.

"What are they doing?" I asked.

"Oh, they are collecting water," Ravi answered. "It rained last night and they are collecting the water from the puddles. They will boil it over fires and use it for cooking and drinking."

My senses reeled. I felt slightly sick. How is that even possible? I wondered. With this filth not just all around them, but in their water supply, how on earth do they survive?

We walked a little closer. The women, and some men who were standing nearby, saw us and stopped what they were doing. They turned and watched us for a moment, then the women stood and took a few steps towards us. I noticed that their faces looked open, neutral, some even appeared to be smiling. Then I chickened out. I felt intrusive, as if my simply showing up in my western-style clothes was a rudeness, an insult.

"Would you like to meet them, talk to them?" Ravi asked.

"No thanks, it's alright. I've seen enough." I replied. I took him by the arm and steered him away, back to the cocooned safety of his car.

We travelled in silence. And as I gazed out of the side window pondering what I had seen I remembered a conversation I had recently had with another Indian friend, "Do you know the main difference between Indians and westerners?" he had asked.

"No," I replied, "Tell me."

"We in India look at those with less than ourselves and we feel fortunate, blessed, grateful, and we are happy with what we have. You in the west look at those who have more, and you feel jealous, hard done by and dissatisfied. You are never happy with your lot."

The words sank in and hit their mark, moving me deeply. Of course, I thought. What we have in our privileged western societies is a sense of lack, of something missing. Without possession of material 'things' to bolster our fragile sense of wellbeing, we have feelings of inadequacy or of worthlessness. We develop a sense of entitlement that justifies our cravings… and we remain deeply unhappy because others have more, and it's not fair. We remain unhappy even when we win, earn or are given more wealth, because our cravings are insatiable and as with an addictive drug we need more and more.

We've developed a significant expectation gap in our wealthy privileged societies, a rift between how we assume our life should be and the reality of it. And our expectation gaps add fuel to our patterns of depression.

Research shows that, indeed, depression is more likely - and starts at a younger age - in affluent countries than in poorer countries. There is an inverse relationship between wealth and depression. Poverty on its own does not necessarily cause depression, and wealth or privilege does not cure it.

Mind the (Expectation) Gap

So mass depression is a modern phenomenon, and it is more prevalent in relatively wealthy countries. What has changed? And why should it be linked more with wealth than with poverty?

One major factor speaks to both questions: our changed expectations, and the modern gap between what we have and what we expect to have.

Consider the role of modern media in creating and shaping not only our role models but also much of our sense of reality in life. Televisions, computers and radios, the colorful artistically designed magazines we read, the dramatic and emotionally evocative movies we watch at the theater, all bombard us with compellingly seductive images of the products we need to make us 'more', to make us complete.

We see the brands of food we need to buy to make us happy, to keep our families satisfied, and to make sure they approve of us. We see the expensive clothes we need to look the part and feel confident, the make-up and perfumes we need to be attractive to our partners, the jewelry, watches, cars, home furnishings, vacations… The list is endless, and the message is always the same: "Happiness must be acquired, must be bought. Something is missing in your life - find yourself here!"

Even when we remain cynical about the advertisers' messages, or about the value or necessity of individual products, the subliminal message gets under our guard and seeps in. We come to believe that happiness is inextricably bound with 'things' and the lifestyle those things bring with them. We have become conditioned to accept that what we really want in life - to feel good, to be happy, to feel confident, complete and at peace - can only be found by acquiring the means, by identifying and attaining something that someone else wants to sell us.

And in our quest for acquired happiness we have become empty consumers: empty because we are always hungry for the next thing, the next fix that we hope will bring some real fulfillment; empty because none of our acquisitions ever fills the void we feel deep inside.

Consider also the types of television shows that are so common today; the ones that masquerade as 'talent' shows, the ones that offer instant celebrity and fame to the lucky, super-talented few. On the occasions I have watched such shows, one factor jumps out at me. It is not the disparity in talent between the various contestants, nor is it the 'me, me, me' attitudes of egos on parade. It is not even the appalling fact that some people with no appreciable talent have been invited on to the shows merely to boost ratings by serving as the butt of cruel humor and ridicule. What strikes me most forcibly is this: almost everyone buys into the notion that celebrity, fame and fortune will save them. Contestants uniformly seem to believe that recognition and success will be the antidote to all their pain in life, will resolve all outstanding issues and render them instantly and forever joyous.

And we, the viewers, buy into this deceit, emotionally willing them on and paying to vote for our favorites to ensure they 'make it' and can live the dream. We desperately want them to break through to success; to find the antidote to their pain, in part at least, I think, because we long for such an answer in our own lives.

We want the fairy tale to somehow still be true. We want to maintain our own vicarious sense of joy, and we want to hold on to the hope that someday our own antidote to pain will be attained. We want to maintain our own illusions, to cling to them as if they are life-or-death forces.

And modern advertising and marketing saturated societies make it easy for us to not only maintain our illusions but to enhance them and pump them up beyond any reasonable expectation.

The Fatal Flaws of Modern Self-Help

The modern self-help and spiritual growth industries also bear some responsibility for feeding into this tendency and further fuelling our depression, because genuine positivity is undoubtedly a great positive force in our lives but forced or fake positivity can truly be counterproductive.

In recent decades there has been a slew of books, cards, videos and other products designed to get us to 'think positively'. Many suggest that we repeat endless affirmations; others proclaim the necessity that we get creative with our inner imaginations and make positive pictures in our heads in our attempts to find happiness and fulfillment. Some books even suggest that the antidote to all our pain is simply to get clear about what we want, write it down in goal-setting fashion and 'put it out to the universe' like some celestial shopping list.

Each of these approaches has a fatal flaw, and some have more than one. The first flaw is this: if we try to alter our thoughts and make them more positive we are simply papering over the cracks. We are approaching the problem from the top down rather than in the effective way, from the bottom up. If we attempt to manipulate our thinking processes simply by imagining and repeating what we would like to be true, we are totally ignoring the fact that our buried and unmet emotions are the causes of our habitual negativities. We will be trying to overlay new conditioning on top of old conditioning.

Let me further explain using a metaphor. I use an Apple Mac laptop computer. Some time ago, when operating system upgrades were still shipped on DVD rather than downloaded over the Internet, I ordered the new 'all singing, all dancing' upgrade that promised to give me all sorts of benefits: increased operating efficiency, more functional stability, new features, and so on. The DVD arrived by mail and I slid it into the DVD drive on my computer and sat and watched.

First the screen went blank, and then a message came up on the screen: Seeking outmoded components of old operating system. A few minutes went by, and then the message changed: Deleting outmoded components of old operating system.

Interesting, I thought. The old stuff needs to be found and removed before the new stuff gets uploaded and integrated. I kept watching until another message appeared: Installing new operating system.

It is the same way with our old conditioning, our old 'operating systems'. We absolutely need to find a way to uninstall the old versions - the outmoded beliefs, vow and promises that have been installed because of our life's experiences - before any new conditioning can be fully effective and beneficial. We need to decondition the old stuff before we can recondition with the new.

So, although I recognize the depressing and potentially harmful nature of repetitive internal negative thoughts, I also know that to change those negativities in an authentic and meaningful way means that we have to change the drivers of the negativities.

When we are willing and able to work at this deep level, the reasons for our negativities are met and the issues resolved. Then our natural positivity can arise and benefit us in myriad ways - automatically lightening our moods, uplifting us, and energizing us, allowing our natural creativities and enthusiasms to fully flow and to become the undercurrent of our lives every day.

The second fatal flaw found in modern self-help books is that nothing we can find, achieve or attain outside of ourselves will ever make us fundamentally happy. Even if we suspend our disbelief in the wishful thinking methods that suggest we can imagine our perfect designer lives into reality, the fact remains that anything we reach for outside of ourselves is of no real or lasting value.

We can see this very clearly when we look at the lives of the rich and famous, the lives of those who seem to 'have it all'. Consider, for instance, the worlds of celebrity and stardom, the lives of the extremely privileged in terms of income and wealth: A-list actors, elite sportspeople, top pop and rock stars, and so on. If we scratch the sometimes-glossy surface and look behind the masks of their public personae, what do we see? Depression is at least as common a phenomenon with these people as it is with the rest of us.

Celebrities who were essentially happy and passionate about their calling before they found wealth and fame are still happy after their lives changed so radically. They might seem grateful for their lifestyles, they might really and truly appreciate and love those lifestyles - but they seem to know that the lifestyle or celebrity does not define them, does not make them who they truly are.

On the other hand, those who were essentially unhappy in their pre-success lives - you know the types I am talking about: the showy, needy, look-at-me, angry, restless, something-to-prove to the world people - remain fundamentally unhappy, restless, incomplete and unfulfilled after they have made it.

For some of this latter group the attainment of their goals or achievement of their dreams seems actually to fuel their unhappiness, driving them to extreme and risky behaviors, booze, drugs and, sometimes, self-destruction. It seems that 'more' in their lives has driven them deeper into desperation and depression.

The Lie of the Need for More

How can this be? There was a time when I got some first-hand insights into the phenomenon.

Though I never actively sought fame, I definitely made the mistake of assuming that depression was somehow inextricably linked with lack, with something indefinable but finite that was missing in life. And I looked everywhere to find it. I always had a plan, an ambition, a goal; always something I was reaching for hoping that it would fill a hole inside me, complete me, be the 'it', the 'thing' that made me finally happy.

I became something of a workaholic and constantly strove to achieve the material things that I thought would be the salve I needed in life. And by the early 1990s that focus, drive and hard work had paid some dividends. I lived in a sizeable house with a large yard and wonderful sea views, drove an expensive sports car, ate in fine restaurants, took wonderful vacations in sunny countries, water skied behind my sports boat, snow skied in France or Switzerland with friends each year… my life was rich by most people's standards, but I was always looking forward, yearning for more, new, bigger, better.

Then something cataclysmic happened, and sent me into a tailspin of desperation.

I was on vacation on the French Riviera, walking along the promenade on the seafront in Cannes. My young former wife, Karen, was pushing a buggy with our cute 18-month-old son, Mark, in it. The sun shone, the sea sparkled and we were in the midst of a culture of style and sun-tanned affluence.

But I still felt incomplete, restless and quietly desperate.

I slowed down and began to trail behind Karen and Mark, distractedly looking out at the Mediterranean, when I saw a motor yacht anchored in the bay. I stopped and gazed as I realized, this was it: this was the next big goal on my achievement list. This navy and white yacht was what I really needed, and I was willing to work my butt off to get it. And when I did, I would feel great, I would feel whole and valuable and complete... everything would be right.

As I dreamed of this goal, a strange thing happened. It felt as if I was whisked off my feet and energetically transported to a party on the stern deck of the boat; I felt as if I owned the yacht, that it was my friends with me partying, drinking champagne, enjoying the high life. I experienced it not at a distance, like some outside observer, but from the inside, as if I was right in the mix, in the middle of the enjoyment and the wellbeing.

In that moment, a dreadful realization arose: in spite of the luxurious trappings, in spite of the attainment, the wealth, the celebration, I was still me - and I still felt fundamentally and unshakably depressed. It was a shattering revelation that I knew to be true. I absolutely, viscerally got it that no material 'thing', no object, nothing on the outside could make me essentially happy. The rug had been pulled on a lifetime belief: that more wealth and the material goods and the lifestyle it could buy would be the antidote to my dissatisfaction and negativity in my life.

I felt devastated. My life plan, it seemed, was broken, laid bare and exposed as a lie. I understood how those who achieve 'everything' risk exposing the great lie that has inspired them, motivated them, kept driving them forward. I got it that even if you achieve the greatest of goals, even if your dreams really do come true, it creates only a temporary high, a 'buzz'. But it does not turn essential unhappiness into essential happiness.

The belief that achieving and living your idealized lifestyle - however you imagine that - will fix your depression is a mistake. Whether you do or do not manage to attain your goals, your underlying issues will still remain. If you fail or only partially succeed in creating the life of your dreams, you will remain unsatisfied. You will still reach for the extra 'something' that will be the fix you need to be happy. You will remain in a drug-addict-like state, looking for the next hit, and the next. You will be on a path of diminishing returns, finding that, no matter how blessed and privileged you really are in life, you need more of everything to keep your illusion in spin.

And you will remain forever unsatisfied.

If you do somehow manage to attain absolutely everything you set out to achieve in life, what then? In all probability you will find that your illusion is smashed; you will discover for yourself the profound disappointment in 'having it all', and will know that your inner baggage still weighs you down, your inner turmoil still festers and robs you of what you are really looking for. If you do manifest your ultimate dreams, what else will there be to look forward to in life? How then will you motivate yourself to keep moving forward with hope?

Telling the Truth About Our Expectations

So, ultimately, it is the belief that the fulfillment of our expectations will save us that is the real problem. Whether or not our expectations are met has little effect on whether we feel depressed or not. And if we recognize this, where does it leave us, what can we do?

Some people suggest simply reducing our expectations. They say that we should be 'realistic' and accept that life is for most of us going to be humdrum, that it is going to be unfulfilling. They encourage us, it seems to me, to 'settle' for what we have and to know that it will lead to an ordinary life that includes suffering. I find that rather depressing.

Thankfully, there is a different approach we can take. We can make an unusual choice: to tell the truth that our fairy-tale aspirations and dreams are an illusion. We can admit to ourselves that succeed or fail, accomplishment and attainment will not resolve our depression issues. Then we can choose to meet and burn through the emotional consequences of letting go of the lie. We can decide to open and fully feel the emotions we have previously avoided - the disappoint-ment, the loss, the disillusionment, and so on - and let them run their course.

We can choose to change our relationship with our deepest feelings so they no longer drive our negativities or cause us to behave in desperate ways. Far from settling for the mundane, we can choose freedom instead of suffering.

The fabulous irony is that when we are willing to do this, to turn inside, face the worst and resolve our deepest issues, we unleash a life force that is capable of creating, manifesting, achieving things in life that were beyond our previous ability to imagine them. When we choose a life of freedom, freedom itself can show up in the most extraordinarily creative and empowering ways in our lives.

We will explore how to do this, in a step-by-step way, in chapter 9. For the moment let's keep on track and explore one more force that adds weight to our depression patterns.

Like the Expectation Gap, this negative force doesn't cause depression all by itself but it can make things a lot worse. It relates to those times when all the things we do to help us to cope don't work anymore, and life threatens to overwhelm us. This is called Coping Strategy Overload. My own story of experiencing this and of finding a way to be free of depression is in the next chapter.

But for now, let me explain this last negative force.

Negative Force #2: Coping Strategy Overload

By the time we reach adulthood most of us have developed a series of coping strategies that allow us to tolerate stressful events and maintain some sense of stability and normalcy in life. For example, we learn various ways to problem-solve so we can feel more 'in control' and take action to alleviate the stress of a situation. Or, as we have previously seen, we learn to manage our emotional responses to stress so we feel differently about our circumstances. But while our strategies may seem reasonably effective to us, and we may feel that we are at least coping with life, we could still be living in a state of low or mild depression.

Coping strategy overload is a condition we experience when the intensity of life's stresses overwhelms our learned ability to cope. This happens when circumstances get so seemingly unbearable or impossible that nothing we do, or can imagine doing, provides an antidote to the pain. This might be because of a one-time catastrophe that quickly overwhelms our ability to cope, or can come about through a series of calamities, when life seems to kick us to the ground and then keeps on kicking. Then life gets so overbearing that coping seems unimaginable and, like a lab rat in an electrified cage with no exit, we collapse, and give up trying to find a way out.

Relationships and marriages can break down and end, loved ones can get sick or die, jobs can be lost and money can run out, homes can be lost, physical and life changing injuries can be sustained, friends can be cruel or abusive. Any such life catastrophe or drama can potentially overwhelm our abilities to cope, and when several such issues hit us at the same time that likelihood increases sharply.

These types of life events have occurred for centuries, but depression has become a pervasive issue only in very recent times. So we need to explore why this is and, ultimately, we need to explore what we can do about it.

Here's the News

We know that our day-to-day lives are massively different from those of our relatives from 50 or more years ago. And one of the main differences that can have an impact on depression is the emotional impact that modern news media have on our lives.

Though it has long been recognized that bad news, drama, and negativity sells - we are, remember, emotional creatures and respond with knee-jerk reactions to emotional stimuli - for a long time the impact of most bad news could mostly be managed, by keeping it away, perceiving it to be at a distance.

Up until the start of the 20th century we got our bad news mostly by word of mouth or by newsprint. When we hear a story or read in black and white about a war, a disaster or a painful drama, it has a manageable impact; it is a story about someone else, somewhere else, and it is easy to disassociate from its emotionality. We can easily maintain a sense of 'us' and 'them', and protect ourselves emotionally by imagining the danger to be remote, to be impersonal or at least not directly threatening in our own lives. Of course, we sometimes go through our own painful experiences in life, but for most of us they are not consistent or relentless, they come and go, they often give us time to recover between stressful bouts of pain.

But since the middle of the last century things have dramatically changed. We now get our bad news beamed directly into our homes, where we watch it on 24-hour television. Vivid and deeply disturbing pictures with loud surround sound now routinely and consistently appear on our large screen TVs, or on our computers and smartphones. So we have made our painful images bigger, closer, more vivid, more clearly focused and much louder. Carnage, inhumanity, aberration and destruction are now inside our sanctuaries, right there in our homes or with us wherever we are; and their emotional impact is incessant and immense.

Our ability to perceive the 'bad' things in life as taking place somewhere else to someone else has been eroded. We can no longer as easily disassociate or shut down to the effect of someone else's suffering, and it overwhelms our bodies' ability to cope. We fall back, normally, on our existing strategies of avoidance and resistance, we play our old games of shutdown and pretense, but the volume and intensity of life's negative stimuli have been turned up, and we find that we need more and better strategies of shutdown; more bracing, more resistance, more self-narcotizing to produce any relief. Our ability to cope, to manage on a daily basis, gets burned out by over stimulus.

The contexts in which our lives play out are generally more intense, more stressful and more overwhelming today than they have ever been in the past. And in this stressful context, when our own lives take turns for the worse those experiences can send us spinning downwards.

The next chapter is my story. I hope that as you read it, you will see some similarity to your own story, and that it will resonate with you and allow you to feel some of the real emotions your own circumstances have brought with them in the past. Maybe it will even allow you to uncover some of the deeper emotions that you might previously have not been able to access, and that would be valuable. If any strong emotion arises just welcome it and, sitting upright with your shoulders back and breathing slowly and deeply, you can allow it to arise, be felt and then naturally subside.

I'll return to introduce the process work in chapter 9.

CHAPTER 8

The Route to Freedom

Overload

During my thirties my experience of depression became distinctly cyclical, and worse. I was focused on my career and often worked long hours. I enjoyed water sports, and periodically put energy into swimming or surfing or water-skiing. For most of the time I managed to function fairly normally, but inevitably, at some point, I'd crash.

I remember lying on the couch on Sunday evenings thinking about the start of another week. There was no 'juice' in the prospect. Life seemed empty, rote and pointless.

I'd wake up the next morning barely able to get out of bed. Often I made myself feel genuinely sick, and was convinced that I was suffering from a cold or virus. I would call work to tell them I was ill, but secretly I knew that I was feeling some general and heavy malaise, not an actual illness. Maybe I'd make it back downstairs to the couch, still in my pajamas, and numbly watch daytime TV. And I would crash for several days, barely moving, barely able to prepare food and eat it, and barely able to climb the stairs each night to get back to bed.

Eventually, I'd get so disgusted and angry with myself that I would drive myself out of my state, and would return to work, to the retail and wholesale jewelry businesses that I ran with my family. I searched for another approach, something else to do, a different way to think, a new way to view life and what it meant: anything that would make me feel better about life.

But I continued to flat line in a meaningless existence. Until the next episode of depression caught up with me. Eventually things really began to unravel.

We lost Mum's parents, Nana and Papa. They died suddenly and unexpectedly only a month apart, both in their mid-70s, and our family was in shock and grieving.

Mum seemed to be coping fairly well; she seemed sad and tender but not devastated or overwhelmed. It was a relief to see her this way because she had suffered from depression, and had been on medication, since she was around 30 years old. We didn't know whether or not the bereavement would tip her over the edge.

About a month after the second funeral, my wife and I went to my parents' house for Sunday lunch. As we chatted over a glass of wine, I noticed Mum touching her underarm as if it were sore.

"What's up?" I inquired. "Is something irritating you?"

"Oh," she answered, I think a little surprised that I had noticed, "I seem to have a lump right here next to my armpit." She indicated. "I'm sure it's nothing much. I've booked an appointment with the doctor this week to get it checked out."

The news unsettled me, but I wasn't unduly worried; after all, armpits were not a body area normally associated with anything serious, were they? I put the conversation to the back of my mind.

Later that week Mum phoned. After hellos and some social niceties, she said, "The reason I'm calling is that I had that doctor's appointment, and he's a bit concerned. He thinks the lump may be cancerous, that I may have breast cancer. He wants me to have a biopsy and then, if worst comes to worst, an operation to have the lump removed. I will be going for further tests next week, and we'll see what happens from there. I just thought you'd like to know."

"Okay," I replied tentatively, "Then I'll keep my fingers crossed. Let's hope it's good news, that it's nothing to worry about. Please let me know as soon as you get the results."

Mum's tests came and went, and confirmed that she did, indeed, have breast cancer. The lump was close to her lymph nodes and the advice was that a full single mastectomy, not just a lumpectomy, was the best option. Mum agreed.

After the operation, while she was still recovering from the anesthetic, Dad called me. "The op went well," he said." And Mum's okay. She's recovering. They just need to do some more tests to find out whether the cancer has travelled into her lymph nodes. Apparently it's more serious if it has gone that far. We'll have to wait and see, and for now, she's a bit groggy, but doing well."

I felt relieved the operation had gone smoothly, and that she was seemingly recovering well, but had a nagging fear somewhere deep inside.

Mum came home after a few days. She looked a little frail but seemed positive, hopeful that it was all over, that she would get the 'all clear'. Then, about a week or so later, Dad called again.

"Mum's surgeon wants to take a meeting with me to discuss her operation. I'd like you to be there too. I've told him we can meet in your office, I hope that's alright."

"Of course," I replied. "Any time. Just let me know."

Dad arrived at my office first. He paced nervously around the room for a few seconds before heading for the kettle and making tea. We waited, making small talk and drinking tea. The consultant arrived.

"What's the news?" Dad asked. "What did the tests show? What's the prognosis?"

The surgeon paused. "Well. It does appear that the cancer cells have migrated into the lymph nodes. That brings with it some difficulties, some complications."

He continued, "Although, every case is different and everyone responds differently to the treatments available, I would say that, on average, we could be looking at about five years."

It seemed surreal, unbelievable.

"So what's the treatment? What can you do for her?" Dad asked. He seemed barely aware of the news he'd been given, like the words had not fully sunk in.

"Well, I'll support you all the way. She will probably have a good two or three years, relatively symptom free. Then we'll see, and we will give her the best palliative care we can."

Dad seemed nervous and dazed. 'So what shall we tell her?' he asked.

The surgeon paused. "It is entirely up to you, of course, but given her depression, given her relative frailty, it may be better to keep the news from her. It may be better, at least in the short term, to tell her that everything went well and that the results came back negative, that she is in the clear."

And we agreed.

Mum recovered from the operation, and our family lives took on an appearance of normality that covered over a multitude of deeper emotions and rendered them inappropriate or at least un-showable.

Inside, I was already triggered into feelings of devastation by the 'death sentence' my mother had been given. I felt dread about the way her life would now play out, and the treatments she would face. I felt a sense of profound emptiness at the thought of living without her in our lives. But these emotions remained buried, unmet and I wrestled with the consequences of our deception: keeping up appearances, remaining positive and enthusiastic as she went through rounds of chemotherapy and radiotherapy. It was stressful beyond belief.

Desperate Wheel-Spinning

And that stress began to take a toll in other areas of my life.

I began to desperately try to find ways to pull myself out of the deep pit of emotions that were hiding inside. My sister, Debs, came back from a business seminar with some audiotapes on self-esteem building and recommended them. I borrowed them and began listening as I drove my car to work one day.

"On a scale of one to ten," the voice on the tape asked, "How would you rate the quality of your life and the way you feel about yourself? If one were pre-suicidal, and ten was perfect, couldn't get any better, where would you rate your life experience - right now?"

I'd not asked myself this question before. Well, I thought, as I checked into my body to feel how it and I felt... I suppose I place it at a three... Three! Is that it?... Yep.

Is this a particularly bad day? I inquired... Nope. It's not a particularly good day, but it's not unusually bad either... So how would you rate a bad day? I asked myself. About one and a half, maybe two. And a good day? Possibly a four... but I don't get those very often.

Wow! I thought. This is shocking.

I continued listening. The speaker used a metaphor: Inside each of us is a shining diamond, pure, pristine and flawless. It's who we really are, though we probably can't see it, don't know it is there. The trouble is that through life's difficulties and pains we get all sorts of stuff thrown at us, and some of it sticks. Judgments, criticism, blame and - you name it. All types of other people's projections come our way, and it's not pretty. Sometimes, we even throw stuff at ourselves, and that sticks, too. Self-blame, self-criticism, internal judgments about who we are and how who we are is not enough, that we are lacking something. Whatever the story, it all lands.

Eventually, our diamond gets covered over with a whole lot of muck. It gets so completely covered that all we see is the dirt, and we come to believe that is all there is, that inside it is only more mess. We forget our own perfection, our purity, our pricelessness. We forget that there is a flawless diamond inside. We forget who we really are.

The words shook me, and deep emotions stirred inside. I choked back some tears and pulled over to the side of the road. "Maybe it's true," I thought "Maybe there is some good in me after all." I began to cry.

I replayed the tape, and as the words sank in deeper I latched on to the idea of a diamond hidden inside me. I saw it. I felt it. I wanted it. And I decided I would do everything I could to uncover it. The teacher on the tape had said that to do this would probably involve some digging around in the muck for a while. He didn't say much that I could understand about how to actually do the digging, but I understood that it was my job to make a decision, to take action, to unearth and clean and polish up this thing.

So I went about it with a vengeance. I missed entirely the point that this diamond is who I already am, who I have always been, and instead I tried to attain it, as if it were some separate thing outside of me. I tried to earn the right to experience the diamond, to have it, instead of resting in the recognition that I am it.

I became desperate to grow, to improve myself, and I looked relentlessly on the outside for what already lay within.

I bought more and more personal growth tapes, on all sorts of subjects like creative visualization and manifesting my ideal life; goal setting and getting clear on my life priorities and vision; never giving up, because you only ever fail when you stop trying; negotiating and getting what I really wanted; mental toughness and so much more. I regularly drove long distances for work and stopped 'wasting my time listening to the ear candy of music' while I travelled. Instead, as soon as I put my seat belt on I would start up the tape player and listen to people who supposedly knew about truly living, about real success, real happiness. I played some of the tapes over and over hoping that what I was learning would become ingrained, second nature to me; hoping that I would become one of the success stories, one of the one per cent who, apparently, had their game together.

I started going to personal growth seminars and spent even more money to listen to people who kept on pushing in life until they 'had it all'. I desperately, manically strove to achieve something that would make me genuinely happy, whole.

After each seminar, or after listening to the latest inspirational tapes, I'd be on a high for a day, or a week, or a month. But the highs were unsustainable. I made more money, bought a boat, learned to water ski, bought the sports car I wanted, moved to a bigger house, bought the clothes that affirmed my image of success, went on vacation to exotic places and got qualified in scuba diving and yet I still felt essentially dissatisfied, still felt rootless, groundless and lost. I was, despite enormous financial and energetic expenditure, still living at a 'three' on the fulfillment scale.

And the recognition that, at my core, I still felt like a failure, as if there was something missing in me, made me more desperate. I repeated the same striving strategies over and over; each time took more energy than the last and each let down made me more defensive and brittle towards others, more stressed.

In the midst of all this forced hyper-activity, my mother developed secondary cancers and quickly began to deteriorate physically. It was soon clear that the cancer had spread, and that she had very little time left to live.

She had more treatment, but this time there was an underlying fatalism, a low level hopelessness about it, though no one spoke it out loud. As in so many previous times in my life I wanted to stop and just cry, but I couldn't. I wanted to shout and yell at God for the cruelty, the injustice, but was blocked, held, emotionally constipated. And I wanted to sit with Mum and tell her how sorry I was, how much I loved her and how grateful I was that she was my mother, and I couldn't do that either. All I could muster was a stream of little presents, tokens that were supposed to show her how I felt. It was pathetic.

The whole family kept the raft of emotional uplift afloat. We became pragmatic, concerned, supportive and caring, while suppressing the hopelessness and devastation that we all felt. It was artificial, and it fooled no one.

Eventually, Mum passed and the emotional dam broke. In the days immediately before and after her funeral, we sobbed and sobbed at death's finality, at the fact that we'd never see her smile again, listen to her kindly, loving words or her endearing malapropisms. We maintained the ritual of family dinners and spoke of the hole, the sense of missing, that her absence evoked. We grieved and mourned in private, and together. I broke down in rage and yelled at God, even though I did not believe in Him, threatening to kill Him for His cruelty, for the extraordinary pain He had wreaked on my mother and on our family.

I stayed open and feeling in the sharp, tender devastation of grief for a few weeks. Then, before it had run its course and struggling with the intensity I was feeling, my personal growth training kicked back in. Surely, I thought, I should be remembering the good things about Mum, should be focusing on the positive aspects of her life and being grateful for what she gave me in life rather than dwelling on the negative. I decided to stop grieving and mourning, and to remember the good times, the fun and the love. I used creative visualizations and focused on the positive things I remembered about Mum and her life. I bought more audiotapes containing subliminal multi-layered positive affirmations masked by sounds of gently breaking waves or whale song. I buried the residual grief and went back to my old ways.

I refocused on new goals, and turned the anxious, nervous energy I regularly felt into action. I tried harder to be a success. I tried harder to be happy. I turned up my efforts to find something, somewhere, that would fulfill me, would define me, make me whole.

My inherent dissatisfaction transferred its focus towards my marriage. Karen, my wife of ten years, didn't understand what I was 'reaching' for, and had no time for all the personal growth work I was addicted to. She wanted a normal, loving, balanced partner, an attentive husband and a caring father to our son. I was none of these things. I began to blame her for not being the partner I wanted, for not 'getting' my aspirations, my drive for a better life. Our relationship became strained and soured.

We were not ones to argue out loud, so our complaints turned inwards and festered resentfully. We spoke less to each other in meaningful or exposing ways, began to carp and gripe about small and insignificant stuff, rather than dig up our real issues and air them. I shut down to her more and more, turned my attention increasingly towards work, and continued with my manic success seeking strategies.

As each desperate attempt to get to what always seemed just out of my reach failed, my actions become mechanical. Like a hamster on a wheel I began to spin with empty, purposeless action. I couldn't stop, but I was going nowhere.

My businesses suffered. My distracted energy had gone elsewhere, my abilities to concentrate and make healthy decisions were eroded, my leadership skills disappeared, and I became increasingly ineffective. I jumped from idea to idea, from plan to plan, without believing any would work. Each was more risky, more desperate than the last. The businesses deteriorated, became unprofitable. Planning turned into firefighting, and daily work turned into a game of 'whack-a-mole' as I tried to beat down each problem that seemed to raise its head.

The pain at home became more than I could cope with, and I told Karen I wanted a divorce. It was heart breaking to see her weep, clinging to our son as if I was trying to steal her lifeblood. I was distraught at the thought of breaking up the family, of leaving not just her, but my son, whom I adored. I braced against the pain, and braced again against the admonishments and pleading of my father and my in-laws to try, for the sake of our son, to make another go of it. But I was resolute. I needed to move on, needed to live the life I was determined to live, and would not be tied down any longer.

We agreed to separate, but agreed that we would still share the same house until it was sold. I moved into a spare bedroom.

I could not sleep. Each night became more disturbed with worries, anxieties and obsessive thoughts of all the mistakes I'd made in life, all the mean and bad things I'd done. I stopped eating and lost a lot of weight alarmingly quickly. I became nervy and could not hold a train of thought for more than a few seconds before falling into confusion.

Business finances became desperate, and we ploughed in our own savings, trying to rescue it. Our bankers increased the pressure to pay down overdrafts and reduce loans, but we couldn't.

A family friend generously offered to invest in our main company, but by now I had nothing left, no energy and no credible plan to save it. It would be a waste I told her, and the loan would never be paid back because the business would still collapse. We met with our bankers and asked that receivers be appointed and the family business, the sacred cow that we had for decades believed could never be allowed to fail, was wound up, finished.

I was officially unemployed, and broke. My sister was unemployed, and also broke. My father, by now in his mid-sixties, was unemployed, nearly broke and, worse, had no pension to support him into old age. The weight of my failure was enormous, the fact that I had let my family down so completely was far worse.

I walked from the bankers' meeting to my car, barely able to stay in a straight line. My legs wobbled, I felt dizzy, spacey, nauseous. Somehow I got home, and sat staring at the stripes on the wallpaper for the next few hours.

I called my doctor and explained some of what I was going through. It was garbled, but he got it. He knew I had a strong dislike of drugs, and said, "You need to see a specialist. I know a psychiatrist who prescribes medication only as a last resort. I think he can help you. I'll make an appointment for you to see him."

The psychiatrist asked what my issue was. I could not articulate it, could barely put a sensible sentence together. He tried a different tack, and asked about my specific symptoms, one by one listing more than twenty of them. "Do you experience, this...? This...?" I nodded or mouthed an almost inaudible "yes" to every one of them.

"You are depressed," he said eventually.

"No shit," I thought, "And I'm paying 100 bucks an hour for this wisdom."

"You have chemical depression," he continued. "That means there is a chemical imbalance in your brain and it is causing depression. We need to address your serotonin levels. I am prescribing some drugs for you."

"So much for the drug-free approach to treating depression," I thought.

He gave me a prescription for Diazepam, Temazepam and Prozac; essentially a mixture of 'downers' and 'happy pills.' I numbly agreed to comply with his regimen.

I had finally crashed, had finally accepted that I was depressed, and felt helpless to do anything except take medical advice. I no longer had any fight left in me. The combination of death, divorce, career failure and, worst of all, the knowledge that I had catastrophically failed my family, so completely overloaded my coping strategies that I had nothing left, and I collapsed. I fell headlong into the black pit of depression as I started on the medication.

I thought I had reached rock bottom, but that was still to come, would be caused by the side effects of the cocktail of drugs I was now taking. I nervously hoped that the medication would return me to normal, would save me, but my saving grace was still some months away.

As summer turned into fall, I had absolutely no clue that within a few short weeks my battle with depression would be over, that I would, once and for all time, be free from its clutches.

Freedom at Last

Some friends persuaded me to join them at a weekend personal growth seminar based on work that I had previously studied, and I reluctantly agreed to go along as a trainer, as someone who would assist others in learning the system and putting it into practice. The idea that I, in my current condition, could help anyone else make improvements in their own lives seemed ludicrous, but I was persuaded to join in.

At the end of the course, while the equipment and products were being packed away, my close friend, Neil, came over. "There were some private sessions available with the presenters. I've booked one for you and one for myself. I know I could use it; I think you could too. It's gonna cost you two hundred quid. You can pay on the day, next Thursday."

I looked at him blankly. "Okay. You'll have to drive us. I'm not up to it."

I had no expectation that the planned session could or would do anything for me; I just went vacantly along with the plan. And I had no idea that what I had signed up for was Brandon's brand-new Journeywork.

Neil and I turned up at a boutique hotel in Chelsea, London, and met our hosts. After a brief preamble one of them, Bill, showed me into a private room and invited me to sit on the couch. He pulled up a chair nearby.

"What is your goal, your desired outcome for the session? "What do you want?"

It didn't even occur to me that I could mention my depression and set a goal to work with it. I said, "Quiet confidence: that's what I'd like."

"Okay" replied Bill, "So what's here right now? What are you feeling?"

I checked. "A bit anxious, as if there's something bad going on deep inside me but I don't know what it is, can't go there, and it's making me feel rattled and edgy."

"Great!" he replied. "So just close your eyes and allow all of that to be here. Really welcome it all and feel it."

Although I couldn't see much that was 'great' about what I was feeling I closed my eyes. I noticed that his invitation had also surprised me. I had been through a lot of therapy and introspective work previously, but this was the first time anyone had shown no professional concern about my painful feelings. Bill actually seemed enthusiastic or encouraged that I was feeling them. And this was, for sure, the very first time anyone had asked me to keep feeling what I was already feeling; they normally wanted me to feel something else. I put my focus on the emotions I was experiencing.

"Just relax," added Bill, "and let whatever you are feeling turn itself up. Let these emotions grow as much as they want to grow."

He paused, and then asked, "Which of these feelings is the strongest?"

"Sadness," I answered. "A deep sadness. That's what is here now." I let the sadness come and grow.

"Wonderful," he continued. "And if there were something deeper than this sadness… If there were an emotion underneath it, what might it be? Just stay open and allow it to arise."

Again, the invitation surprised me, caught me off guard. Bill appeared to be asking me just to feel whatever I was feeling, and the invitation was disarming, it caused me almost automatically to soften my body and let go of my normal bracing against and suppression of feelings.

I did not recognize it at that time, but for the second time in my life I started to drop down through the emotional layers. And this experience was to be even more profound than the first.

"Lost." I answered. "I feel like I'm completely lost, that I don't know where I am or even who I am."

"Okay. So staying open, experiencing this, and then exploring even more deeply… What comes next? What feeling is underneath lost?"

I allowed myself to fall right into the heart of whatever was coming next, time after time. I was not a particularly good client, and sometimes I could make pictures but could not identify the emotion that I was feeling, and sometimes I wrestled and resisted the process, but eventually at each level a distinct emotion appeared, and I felt it. And at each level we went deeper, further down the feeling chain.

Lost turned into hurt, hurt into desperation, desperation into rage, rage into fear and fear into hopelessness. Hopelessness became overwhelm and, eventually, when I had allowed overwhelm to be completely and absolutely overwhelming, I arrived at a place that seemed like a stopping point, like the end.

"What's here now?" asked Bill.

"It's the end," I replied. "Death. It feels like I will die if I go there."

"That's beautiful," he answered. "So go there. Just stay awake, be present to the experience, and open to allow death to be here. Stop resisting it. Welcome it."

I had no resistance left, and I decided to surrender. If death wanted me then death could have me, could take me. I had had enough. I let go into it.

I felt a dissolving sensation, as if reality was deconstructing, life ebbing away. It felt final, as if everything had reached its end and was disintegrating, dying.

A few minutes passed, then Bill's soft voice intervened: "And when death has destroyed everything, taken everything, what remains? In the heart of death, in its essence, what is here?"

The question made no sense - it had nowhere to land, nothing to engage with. I had no religious or spiritual beliefs: after death was the finality of nothing - end of story.

"Nothing," I replied, almost silently, though indignantly. "Absolutely nothing."

"Fabulous," Bill answered. "Just welcome this absolute nothingness; really welcome all of it."

He paused for a short while and then continued. "And if there was something in the heart of all nothing, something right in its essence... what might that be? What is it?"

The suggestion that there might be 'something' in the heart of 'nothing' made no sense, but I tentatively explored and let my awareness probe into the heart of this void. Its infinite greyness began to get lighter, at first like a weak flashlight, barely able to penetrate a dense fog, then getting progressively brighter and brighter until in time the flashlight turned into a golden yellow sun that burned through the clouds, clearing them and dazzling my eyes.

"Light!" I said, in amazement. "There's light here. Everything is light - it's everywhere!"

"Excellent!" replied Bill. "You are doing great... So now just allow everything to open into this light. What is its essence? What is its true nature? If you just allow yourself to be carried into the heart of this light, what's here? What is exposed?"

My experience unfolded with his words. It seemed as if life pulled back the drapes that had hidden its own true magnificence, and its - my - true nature was revealed.

"Love," I said. "It's love! And it's everywhere. It's divine, pristine, absolute... It's omniscient, universal. There is no beginning and no end to it. I don't have the right words, it can't be properly described. It's silent, vast and beautiful. There is no individual 'me', there's just This... It just is... "

The experience blew me apart. The realization that at the core of my being was the diamond I had for years been seeking was more than my thinking mind could hold. The diamond I had uncovered did not look the way I had expected; in fact, it didn't look much at all like a diamond. This glorious gem was immeasurably more stunning, more precious than anything my mind could have conceived.

This diamond was not finite but infinite, and I realized that it was my true essence, that it was me and I was it. I sat awestruck as Bill continued the session.

He invited me to imagine the convening of a campfire of truth, one where anyone associated with my deepest pains, my most potent past issues, would be welcome. In my mind's eye I saw the orange glow of the campfire and got a sense that my parents should be there. I welcomed images of them. They showed up looking much younger, as if they were aged somewhere in their 30s. I let Bill know they were present.

"Good," he answered. "So now welcome a younger version of yourself to be present. This could be a version of you at a specific younger age, or a version of you that embraces an age range; either will be fine. And then there is, of course, the present day version of you, also here at the campfire."

I welcomed both. It seemed as if the younger me had a flexible age of somewhere between 7 and 14. It was a strange and exposing feeling to get a sense of the youth, the naivety, the desires, expectations and frustrations of my younger self. Memories began to arise; all were about the way I felt controlled and powerless as a child, as if my options had been taken away and I was being suffocated by my parents' rules, by their sheer willpower. I started to feel angry.

"Now welcome a mentor to this campfire," Bill continued. "It can be someone you know or someone you know of, or it can be someone born from your own imagination. This is a very wise being, maybe a sage or a saint, in whose presence you can rest and trust."

I imagined an old Chinese sage with long flowing white hair and beard. He looked a little like David Carradine's kung-fu mentor from the 1970s television series, the one who prefaced each teaching with, "Ah, Grasshopper..." His presence seemed deeply wise and protective.

My instructions continued. "And so, with everyone sitting in the protective presence of this campfire of truth, in the loving and wise embrace of the mentor, and with everyone feeling safe and willing to speak the truth about what was experienced and what was felt in the past... If the younger you could speak, from his heart about some old pain, some old hurt... to whom would he like to speak first?"

"Dad," I said emphatically.

The anger that had been welling up turned into rage. There was no controlling it and I let rip. Quietly but with huge intensity, I spilled out all the words that I had shut down, suppressed, choked back as a child: words that spoke with furious hurt about feelings of being controlled, having no choice, being powerlessness, trapped and negated as a person. The sheer power of the energy behind the words shocked me, but there was no holding back. On and on I went, naming times, giving examples of how and when I had felt hard done by, mistreated, unfairly judged and punished, arbitrarily controlled, dismissed and made to feel insignificant. Dad just sat there and listened, as I emptied out every blaming word I could find to describe how it felt to have him as a father.

Eventually, the flow of words wound down and there seemed to be nothing more to say. I still felt supercharged energy, but the energy seemed mute. I told Bill I was finished.

"So," asked Bill, "If your father, having heard these words from his young son could reply, not from his ego but from his heart, what might he reply? If he were to reply from the deepest part inside, from the level of the soul, what would he want the younger you to know? What would he really say?"

I waited. Dad looked red in the face, seemed to be close to tears. He nodded his head, as if in recognition, at least, of what had been shared. He mouthed the words, "I'm sorry." Then he turned to his right where, as if out of nowhere my grandfather, his father, appeared. My father pointed at Gramps, as if to blame him. In the same way I was blaming my father for my pains, he seemed to be blaming his own father.

Gramps turned to his right, and his father appeared. Gramps pointed the finger of blame. And suddenly a huge procession of men appeared, generations that trailed back through eons of time. Each man pointed at his own father in blame. The chain seemed endless: blame, blame, blame, reaching further back in time than my eyes could see, than my mind could conceive.

So what? I silently thought. We all blame our parents? Every one of us that has ever existed blames the people who came before them? Where does that end? How far back does that really go? Does it go right back down our evolutionary chain? Who is ultimately to blame? Where did this mistake begin? With a monkey? With a fish? With a single-celled-something we would barely recognize as a living animal? The questions tumbled through my mind.

But that's ludicrous, I thought. I burst out laughing. "That's nuts," I exclaimed out loud, "It's insane!"

The whole lineage of men gradually disappeared, and my father and I looked into each other's eyes. "I'm sorry for the blame, Dad." I said. "I'm sorry for my judgments, sorry for the shutdowns, the resistances. I'm sorry for being such a pain in the ass."

"I forgive you," he answered. "We all do it, in one way or another. Would you please forgive me for whatever I did to hurt you? Please know that I have only ever wanted you to be safe and happy in life."

"Absolutely!" I answered. "Of course I will."

Any remaining resistance inside me seemed to break wide open, and it felt as if the energy of forgiveness flowed from me to him, and from him to me. We hugged in silence. It felt complete.

I turned to Mum, who was still sitting quietly at the campfire. This time the words seemed to come from the present age me, and I spoke to her much more quietly than I had begun with Dad; from a more vulnerable place, a place more willing to share from old hurt than needing to blame.

"You know I felt hurt and angry at you for some of the things you did to me when I was a child?" I asked. Some memories of her being brittle and dismissive arose.

"Yes," she answered, "I see that."

"I just wanted you to know," I said, "Just wanted you to know how it felt when you threw your tantrums and said hurtful things. That's all."

"I'm so sorry, Kev," she added, "I was really struggling too. I was in pain. I didn't know how to be a better parent, didn't know how to cope any better than I did, and I'm really, truly sorry."

"Thank you," I replied, "I think I needed to hear that. I would like to apologize to you too. I can see how my naughtiness and willfulness must have upset you. I know I was a bit of a handful to bring up. I'm really sorry for the distress I caused you. I didn't mean it."

"Thanks," she answered, "Me too... I forgive you, I mean. Of course I forgive you, with all my heart."

Again the energy of forgiveness flowed both ways. When it was complete, it seemed as if something - maybe some old story, maybe some old projection of blame, definitely some old hurt - was over. Something painful just stopped being painful. There was deep peace palpable in everyone.

My parents, the younger me, and the present me stood up and embraced in a four-way hug. We were bathed in sublime unconditional love.

Then the mentor spoke: "When you open your heart and empty out all the old stuck words and emotions from old traumas and pains, when you have said everything you need to say, all the things you could have or should have said at that time; when you have been rawly, deeply truthful and there is nothing else left to say on the matter, forgiveness is the natural result. You have witnessed that, right here at this campfire. And forgiveness clears the way to unconditional love. Together, forgiveness and love are the most healing forces on this planet."

Bill invited my parents to merge into the light of the campfire, asking me to cut any unhealthy cords or ties that still might exist with them and send them love and blessings as they merged.

Then he asked me to hug the younger me and, as we spoke to each other, reassured and forgave each other, asked that the younger me merge into the body of the present day me, allowing the younger me to grow up inside me with the forgiveness, completion and unconditional love already present.

As this happened, it felt as if the 'reality' of my past was transmuted, as if old memories of hurt were salved and old grievances resolved. It felt as if my cells were healing, my whole body vibrating at a higher frequency; at the deepest level it felt as if something had positively shifted in my DNA, as if my genes were preparing to express 'me' in a new and more wholesome way.

Eventually, Bill brought me back into the present, into the room we were in and I opened my eyes. I was shocked to find out that two hours and twenty minutes had passed; it had seemed like only fifteen or twenty minutes.

There was nothing to say. There was no way to explain, to articulate, what I had gone through or was experiencing. I nodded mutely at Bill, and he gently shepherded me out of the consulting room into a communal area, where Neil was waiting with Brandon, who had been his facilitator.

All I managed to say was "Thank you."

I was absolutely calm, totally present to the moment. For the first time that I could remember I felt whole, complete. My body and my mind felt like they had been spring-cleaned; I felt pure, spotless, as if all life's stains had been completely washed out of me. I was at peace with myself and I tingled with bliss.

I knew, absolutely and beyond all doubt, that my struggle with depression was over. I knew with total certainty that the darkness I had experienced for nearly 30 years had not just lifted but had left for good. I knew for sure that not only had I finished with it, but that it had finished with me.

As I rode home in the car I thought about the medications that lay waiting in my bathroom cabinet, and I knew that I did not need them, that my body and my mind neither required nor wanted them.

I knew, categorically, irrefutably, that depression was no longer a part of me, no longer present in my life; that it never again would be. My life was starting afresh, and though no circumstance had changed, everything was different.

I knew I was free.

A Brand New Life

Though I did not know it at the time, I was one of the very first beneficiaries of Brandon's newly developed Journeywork, the work that has since that time profoundly changed the life of hundreds of thousands of people from all backgrounds, from all walks of life, from so many different traditions, cultures and religions around the world.

It is now 24 years since that session, and for those two-plus decades I have lived completely free from depression; more than that, I have lived with an undercurrent of wholeness, fulfillment and positivity in my life. I have been naturally, inherently happy – completely free from all depression-related medications.

These years have not been particularly smooth, nor have they been 'ideal' or 'perfect' in the way my mind might have imagined. They often have been tumultuous. There have been times of excitement and adventure, of deepest love and bliss, of inspiration and ecstasy. And there have been times of deep disgruntlement, of insecurity, tensions, fears, arguments and pain, even of extreme stress.

But depression has been nowhere in the mix.

For 24 years my body, mind, being, soul, have without doubt known two things. The first is that for me, now, emotional openness is a natural choice. I can choose to remain open emotionally and authentically feel whatever life triggers. I can choose to drop the story surrounding any of my emotional responses, and although the experience may be temporarily intense, I can choose to simply feel whatever pure emotions are present. Whenever I do so, those emotions can arise, be fully felt and pass through my body quickly, leaving me feeling refreshed, spacious, at peace.

The alternative is that I could choose to shut down, to put a lid over or brace against my emotions, maybe helping the process along by getting hooked into the story that has triggered me. It is a pattern I remember all too well, but the shutdown would ultimately be too painful, too long lasting, would be unthinkable today.

So I choose openness. I choose to feel all of life, to live and engage and experience every single bit of it.

The second realization that I have lived with is even more profound and life changing: it is the realization of who I am. I live in deep gratitude for the fact that I was shown a way to wake up to a truth that I had long been searching for. I live in gratitude for the absolute recognition that at my core resides no personality, no role or any 'thing' that can be identified with; at my core, my essence, resides infinite wholeness, universal love, a spaciousness so vast that it includes everything and nothing. This realization is predicated on no religious, spiritual or other belief. It is simple and self-evident. It needs nothing, is already fulfilled. It is all-inclusive, always complete.

Each morning when I awaken, this truth reveals itself freshly. And the whole of my life is now lived richly, in the context of this realization.

I am That which I had been seeking.

Now it's your turn. This is your invitation to experience freedom from depression, once and for all. In the next chapter you will find processes developed to get at the roots of your depression and help you find clarity, peace, equanimity - whatever word represents the life you would lead if depression were no longer part of it. **Please, do the work: freedom lies on the other side.**

CHAPTER 9

The 'How To': Journey Process Work

It is time to do some introspection and clearing work. We will take things step-by-step so it can be as straightforward as possible.

Whatever else you engage with from this book, please give yourself the benefit of doing this work! It can do for you what was done for me and for many thousands of others - it can cut right to the core causes of depression and pull them out by the root.

We start with some activities, a bit like the ones we've done earlier in the book. We call them introspections. The introspections have been developed and refined over more than two decades. They've been used successfully, often with extraordinary healing and transformational results, by hundreds of thousands of people around the world. It is work born not from theory but from our direct experience and it creates visceral, real-life results when you are willing to roll your sleeves up, get real and open authentically with some emotions, allowing yourself to stop resisting them, relax, and experience them fully.

Some of the processes you'll go through are non-emotional or only mildly emotional. Others can be deeply emotional, and for these you should remember that any emotion will pass quickly - normally within seconds to a couple of minutes maximum - if you allow it all to be felt, just let it wash through you.

And don't forget that no emotion, no matter how intense, can ever harm you. If you surrender completely to feeling any emotion it will feel ultimately purifying; it will cleanse you and leave you feeling free and at peace. It is only the stories we add to emotions, the games we play with them, that cause us problems by turning that emotion into a mood or a state.

You'll need to work through each introspection separately, in the order presented. Once you have done them all you can return and repeat any of them at any time. The important thing to start with is that you do them in this order first, working through the processes that will enable you to tackle the root of your depression.

It's best to approach them all with humility and genuine curiosity, like a deeply personal experiment, a true inquiry into your own essence and the essence of truth itself. You'll need to leave a break between each introspection. It's good to do them on separate days so that your body and mind have time to take in the changes that are happening. But if you want to get on we've indicated how long to break between each one.

Some of the introspections are longer than others. The specific instructions for each one tell you how long it may take.

You'll need a clean and welcoming space to work in where you can sit comfortably. And you'll need to get rid of distractions so make sure to tell people around you that you should not be disturbed. Turn off all phones, and give your inner focus entirely to the work in hand for as long as it lasts.

You'll remember that a man called Bill guided me through my first, and life changing, experience of this process. You will also need someone to be with you. You've got two options here, and both of them are good so pick whichever feels right for you.

> • If you choose to do this face to face with a real person then pick someone you trust and who is willing to support you emotionally. This person does not need to have any particular qualifications, all they will need to do is read the instructions and read the scripts at a pace that suits you, and write some simple things down - so make sure they have a pen and paper with them. The introspections are scripted in a way that we know will guide you safely through the process. The scripts that they will need are at the back of this book or are downloadable from

www.kevinbillett.org/book-bonus. In all scripts whenever they see … it means that they should take a short pause.

• Alternatively you can listen to an audio recording of each process, and let me guide you through it by going to www.kevinbillett.org/book-bonus. This is my preferred way for you to work if you can get online and download the audio files, because this way is easier and you will be more able to relax and be fully present to the experience.

If you are using the online recordings it's useful, though not essential, if you use headphones and if you listen on a device that allows you to easily pause the play from time to time. This means that you can take time to digest or answer out loud some of the questions I will ask. You may also need to softly open your eyes and write something down, so make sure you have writing material ready.

We want to you to feel ready to let yourself do the work so each introspection has a title and a short description of where it comes from and what it's for. We've also included the time it will take and give you a heads up on how emotional it might be and whether you'll need time to rest afterwards.

Now enjoy the ride… and later you can celebrate the results!

Instructions: The Conscious Decisions Process

Download the audio and script at www.kevinbillett.org/book-bonus

Intention:
That you make the choice to positively change some aspect of your life
Time:
40 to 45 minutes
Emotional level:
Mildly to moderately emotional
What you need:
Pen/paper
At the end:
Short break of 30 minutes or so.

This process is adapted from a well-known Neuro-Linguistic Programming intervention that has been used for many years. We have adapted it here for our specific uses, and it is a great place to start.

It will allow you to get clear about the future consequences and feelings you might experience if you live life without changing your fundamental approach to it - if you continue to go with the old flow, or let things slide without making some firm decisions to change.

This possible experience is then contrasted with the future in store for you if you do open emotionally and make some changes in life - even if you don't yet know how those changes might be possible.

It is not necessary to 'see' everything clearly in this process. It is a process that works just as well when you just get a sense or an inner knowing in answer to some of the questions. That sense, or inner knowing will be more than adequate for you to make the choice to positively change some aspect of your life.

Exercise 6: The Conscious Decisions Process

Make yourself comfortable, and as you close your eyes you can just begin to relax. So, just take a nice deep breath in... and let it slowly out... and another long deep breath in... and slowly out... coming to rest... and opening in your being... softening your body... letting go... Now turn all attention inside... letting your long, deep breaths cause your body to relax even deeper... and allowing all awareness to rest in the spaciousness inside.

And now just allow your thinking mind to relax... let all thoughts... and pictures... and words... slowly fade, dissolve... and let the mind come to rest, like a ceiling fan whose power has been turned off at the mains...

As you continue to relax and open... you may notice in your mind's eye, or you may get a sense or knowing, that in front of you is a downward-facing staircase... and this shimmering staircase has five steps... And in the knowledge that these steps will lead you deeply in to your essence... in to the deepest, innately wise and all-revealing part of you... step now onto the top step, number five...

*With each step taking you deeper into your own true self... stepping down onto step four... opening down to three... deeper down to two... and before you step onto the final step, step one... just let your awareness expand infinitely in front... and behind... allow consciousness to become boundless to each side... open spaciously above... and deepen ocean-like beneath... Then step into the core of your own deepest awareness... as you step down onto step one now... and just rest **as** this awareness...*

Now you may notice that to one side of you is a doorway... And in the knowledge that through this doorway is the light of your own soul... and that waiting here is a mentor of freedom... one in whose divinity and wisdom you can rest and trust... just walk through the doorway, in to the light... and greet your mentor... thanking him or her for being here to assist you... Great.

And now just allow the mentor to walk you to one side where there is a special area with the choice of two paths... they represent different life paths, with different consequences for the future, depending on different choices in the present moment... So just allow the two paths - one a left hand path, and one a right hand path - to arise in awareness... Great.

The left hand path is the path of life when you make no changes to your current strategies and choices and habits... This is what the future holds when the current levels of shut down and resistance to life remain unchanged... when you go with the status quo, or allow things to slide, and continue to avoid some key personal issues, letting life go the way it is already heading... Along this path the consequences of remaining asleep or stuck in existing patterns and behaviors become truly apparent.

So, letting the mentor guide you, just take a walk down the left hand path... stepping into the future a week... and a month... and now a whole year... and **see and hear and feel** how life unfolds when you fail to address or wake up to some of your core life issues... when you make no changes in yourself, and you let life carry on the way it has been going.

Really get a full sense of what it is like to be living your life... as you walk down this path... Look around... What unfolds?... What happens?... How does life play out?... And how does that **feel** one year down the line?... [Let answer]... Okay.

And now step into the future two years down the line... just let the time line extend... and **see and hear and feel** how life continues to unfold from the base of having failed to make some significant changes... **really open to the consequences of remaining limited in some significant areas of life**... take a good look around you... notice how others are responding to you... how circumstances are evolving... and feel how it really feels to be living life this way... So how does it feel?... [Let answer]... Okay. Thank you.

So now allow the time line to unfold further, carrying you five years into the future... The results of avoidance or inaction have been in play for five more years in your life... So **see and hear and feel** how life is showing up now... **Really step into the reality of how life is being lived** when you neglected to make some healthy choice in the past... and get a full sense of what things are like, how life feels... How does that feel?... [Let answer]... Okay.

And now ask the mentor to take you a whole decade down the line... and just step ten years into the future... Let life evolve the way it would when you fail to make some important choices... when you just keep going with the same old, same old... and again, **see and hear and feel** how it is to be living this life, at this time... Is it fulfilling?... **Does it feel right, and true, and purposeful?... Is it rewarding and liberating?... Or not?...** How is it to be living this life at this time?... How does it all really feel?... [Let answer]... Okay. Thank you.

And so now you can ask the mentor to softly bring you back through time... back to the present moment, where you are facing the choice of two paths in life... You've experi-

enced what the left hand path has in store... And you can now begin to contemplate the right hand path... the path of healthy choice... the path you take when you face up to some core issues and deepen in freedom...

So, as you contemplate embracing the specific changes that would be necessary in your life to take the right hand path, the path of liberation... just take a moment, and put out an intention that pure awareness reveals the choices that need to made right here... What needs to be embraced in life?... What does life itself want you to admit to yourself and to face?... What does life invite you to get real about?... And what veils or restrictions or limitations, what old patterns or behaviors or habits or beliefs does life invite you to free yourself from?... How does life really want you to grow and evolve?... [Give time, let answer. Be gently encouraging]... Great.

And so now turn to the mentor and ask her or his help in getting clear about something: What emotional resources would you need?... What qualities could you really do with in order to confidently decide and commit to healthy change... to get real and embrace the fullness of life?... What resources would you choose?

You might choose confidence or certainty, you could choose self-love or self-worth... you could choose trust, inner strength or willpower... you might like a sense of lightness, or humor, or childlike curiosity... Or the ability to communicate clearly and effectively... You could choose the knowledge of yourself as the infinite, as divine... If you could choose anything and everything you needed, what would be chosen? ... [Give time, let answer. Be creative and encouraging, write down any answers received]... Great.

And so now, let the mentor give you a large colorful bouquet of balloons... with each balloon containing one of the empowering resources you have chosen... one by one, just breathe in each quality... feeling it flood through every cell of your being... right down to the cellular level... permeating right down to your DNA, and into your genes... and ultimately saturating the spaces between the spaces ... [Name each resource and allow time to breathe it in.]... until the being has everything it needs to make the healthiest of choices and commitments.

*And then, speaking out loud the decisions and commitments that you are now empowered to make... the healthy choices that you now embrace in life... [Let yourself speak these out]... And allow the mentor to guide you as you take a walk down the right hand path... the path of freedom, of authentic self-expression and fullness of life... and step a week, a month, and a year down the line... and **see and hear and feel** how life now unfolds... now that healthy decisions are supporting you and unfolding naturally... Just* get a full and vivid sense of how differently you experience life now... So what is happening?... How is life showing up?... [Let answer]... Good.

Now step into the future two years down the line... and allow life to take its natural course, based in healthy awareness and choice... Let it evolve and grow the way it does when empowering change is embraced... and see and hear and feel how it is to be you... to be living this way... to fully embrace life and to be embraced by life... How does it really feel to be living this way... two years in the future?... [Let answer]... Great.

And now step five years into the future... You have experienced five years of deepening and growth... all because some healthy decisions were made when life asked it of you... And life has played out in some very specific ways... maybe also in some unexpectedly wonderful ways, because of the choices you made all that time ago... And **see and hear and feel how great it is to be living a life of empowerment and freedom... how extraordinary it feels to be awake and fully alive.**

Notice how your relationships have grown and deepened... with those you really care about... with those who care about you... with yourself... Notice how differently you are communicating, internally and externally... See how differently you are acting and engaging with life... And feel how differently you feel about yourself... about life... So how does all this feel?... [Let answer]... Wonderful.

Finally, invite the mentor to take you a full decade down this path... and step into the future ten whole years... having lived a rare and conscious life... having been true and authentic to yourself... following a path that is true and right... and deeply fulfilling... and **see and hear and feel** how good it is to be alive... how blessed it feels to **be** the awareness, the grace that animates all of existence... Really open fully and completely into the truth of how it is to live in freedom... What is taking place?... What does life reveal?... And how does it feel to be you, the real you, living in this way?... [Let answer]... Excellent.

And as you let the reality of this existence settle and permeate every fiber of your being... you can just allow the mentor to bring you back to the present moment... knowing that time is just an illusion, and that any awareness that arises is available in the present moment...

Then ask the mentor if she or he has any words of advice, or wisdom to share with you... If there were anything to say, what would the mentor offer?... [Let the answer arise]...

Great... So you can thank the mentor for the words, and for being a grace-filled guide on your path of exploration today... [Give time]... And then walk back through the doorway and over to the bottom of the stairs you first came down...

And then, just step back up the steps... **one***... feeling uplifted and energized...* **two***... feeling refreshed and renewed...* **three***... stretching and becoming aware of the body...* **four***... and pausing for a moment right here on step four... And knowing that when you eventually step up onto step five, that you will only be able to open your eyes as soon as all parts of you are fully integrated and agreed that Freedom is who and what you are, and that anything that is needed for you to make healthy and conscious decisions and choices in life is always here, already present and available inside you; that you have always been and always will be the purest of divine presence... And when all parts of you are in agreement you can step up onto step five now... and take a good long deep breath in... and let it all the way out... And you may open your eyes now, when you are ready...*

Congratulations! Wonderful work.

Instruction: Please give your partner a few minutes to come around, and then ask them to write down in a notepad what decisions and commitments they are making.

Instructions: The Physical Journey Process

Download the audio and script at www.kevinbillett.org/book-bonus

Intention:

That you uncover the 'cell memory' associated with some old hurt, upset or trauma, then that you verbally empty out any words associated with an old hurt or trauma, and forgive and resolve that issue, heal from it

Time:

60 to 90 minutes

Emotional level:

Moderately to deeply emotional

What you need:

Quiet space. Pen and paper. Tissues

At the end:

Short break of 30 minutes or so

The Physical Journey process is a Journey classic. It has been used since the beginning of Journeywork to help people clear the residual effects of old traumas hurts, and upsets - the ones that have lodged cellularly and may have caused us emotional or physical difficulty over the long run. It is a deeply resolving introspection that has produced fabulous healing and transformational results for large numbers of people. It is an important step in our journey of clearing the root causes of depression, and it has been adapted here specifically for use with depression - and it is easy!

The Physical Journey is an inner exploration, and you can treat it just like a game of adventure. Many children around the world have shared this process (or a slightly simpler children's version of it) with other children. So if they can do it, so can you!

This introspection should take approximately one to one-and-a-half hours to complete, and it is advisable to take a little additional rest time afterwards, so make sure you allow sufficient time. As always, make sure that you have a quiet space and that you will be uninterrupted.

Exercise 7: The Physical Journey Process

*Allow yourself to find a comfortable position, and when you're ready, just close your eyes... And as you feel yourself sitting in your chair... as you hear the sounds in the room... and as you feel your breath gently going in and going out, you may begin to feel yourself **relax**... And as you hear the sound of my voice, and as you feel your back resting against the chair... and with every breath you take, you may begin to notice that it is **causing** you to **relax**... deeper and deeper... more and more relaxed, opening into your essence... into your very Source...*

Imagine in front of you a downward facing staircase... there are 10 steps... Can you see them, or get a sense of them?... [Let answer]... Good... This is an extraordinary staircase because it can carry you ever deeper into the vast presence of freedom that is your own true nature. And the good news is, you don't have to do a thing... just step on each step and the staircase will carry you effortlessly deeper.

And before you step on the top step, just take four large, colorful balloons, and, as you do... just breathe in the qualities of these balloons... openness... breathing that in... and willingness... breathing that in... and trust... breathing in trust... and lastly, a childlike curiosity... breathing in curiosity... Great.

And now, when you're ready, go ahead and step onto step number 10, the top step ... Now step onto the next step, step 9... now 8... With each step you take it is drawing you deeper and deeper into the boundless awareness, the presence of Source... Now step onto step 7... 6... 5... Just allow yourself to relax ever deeper with every step you take... 4... 3... expanding and allowing yourself to go deeper and deeper... 2... and now, as you get ready to step onto the bottom step, step 1, allowing awareness to expand in front of you... Now feeling a boundless presence expanding behind you... a vastness extending infinitely to either side of you... a spaciousness opening underneath you... and a vast expansiveness above... Just rest in the experience of ever-deepening boundlessness... letting your Self grow still and silent in the ever-deepening expanse... 1... And just rest in the awareness of your Self as Source...

The Shuttle Ride & Discovery

Now, imagine a thermometer in the ground. It has numbers going from 1 to 10... 1 is the deepest you can go, and 10 is refreshed, alive waking consciousness. If you can't exactly see the thermometer, that's perfectly fine... Just get a sense or knowing that it's there... Now, if 1 is the deepest you can go into Source, and 10 is full, bright waking consciousness, can you get a sense of where you are on the thermometer?... You may actually hear a number, or see it rise to a certain level, or just get a sense or a knowing about what number you are at... So where are you on the thermometer?... [Let answer]... Can you let the thermometer rise by a half point?... [Let answer]... Good... Can you let it fall by 1 point?... [Let answer]... Good... Now that you know exactly who is in charge, at what number would you like it to rest?... [Let answer]... Great... You can just allow that to happen naturally of its own accord, letting the same part of you that makes your heart beat, your eyes shine and your hair grow draw you ever deeper into your deepest self, into the vast, boundless presence in the core of your being.

Now imagine a door in front of you... Behind that door is blazing light... the light of your own being, your own Source... and the nature of this light is boundless love, infinite freedom... Also behind this door is your mentor of freedom, of liberation... one in whose wisdom you can trust, and in whose presence you feel safe and protected... It can be someone you have heard of or someone imagined... a saint, a sage or enlightened being or a divine presence... and it is someone in whose expansive realization and wisdom you can rest... So, when you are ready, just step through the door into your own light and greet your mentor... And you can nod your head to let me know when that has happened... [Give time]... Great.

Now imagine a space shuttle in front of you... This space shuttle is a very special vehicle... It can take you to any part of your body, no matter how small or large... and it knows exactly where to go... It can go inside your organs, in your veins, muscles or tissue in a very graceful, safe and protected way... Now go ahead and let you and your mentor step inside... Are you inside?... Good... Now, when you are ready push the blue button on the dashboard, the one that is already marked 'Depression Root Cause'... and let the shuttle take you to your first stop... It may not be where you expect to go... so just allow the shuttle to be your guide. It is powered by your own body wisdom... so let your innate wisdom take you where it wants to go, and when you arrive, be sure to bring the shuttle to a full stop, pull on your handbrake and let me know... [Wait for answer. Encourage if necessary]... Good.

So, do you have a sense yet of where you might have arrived?... [Let answer]... Great... Go ahead and with your mentor step outside the shuttle with big flashlights in your hands... What does it feel like under your feet?... What does it look like?... Can you describe what the area is like?... Do you get the sense that you are inside or outside the organ, or the place you feel you should be?...

Instruction: If outside, and they would like to go inside, say: "Imagine a small doorway that will allow you inside, and let you and your mentor step directly into the core of this organ (or muscle or tissue)." If in doubt, ask mentor's advice.

Memory Elicitation

Now put your flashlights on high beam and take a good look around... What does it look like?... Explore the whole region... Just get a sense of what it's like and describe it to me... [Let reply]... Are there any areas that sort of stand out to you, or look different from the rest of the region?... Take your time... keep walking around and really take a close look at what it's like in there... you don't have to see it exactly... Just get a sense of it, or an inner knowing... [Give time]... Now go over to the area that seems somehow different than the rest... Let your mentor guide you there... What does it look like?... You and your mentor can stand right next to it... If it had an emotional feeling pouring from it, drenching you, I wonder what feeling that might be?... If there were an emotional feeling just pouring over you, and if you had to give a name to that feeling, what might that be?... [Let answer]... Allow yourself to experience the feeling fully... Let your whole being be suffused with it.

Then, ask yourself, "When have I felt like this before?" and in answer to this question, in your mind's eye, look down at your feet and see what, if any, shoes you are wearing... "When have I felt like this before?" and in your mind's eye look down at your feet and see what you are wearing or not wearing... Look at your legs and at your clothes... Get a sense of how old you feel yourself to be, and where you might be... Who else is there?... Does the person or people evoke a certain memory or a series of memories?... [Give sufficient time to answer. Encourage]... Great.

Now imagine putting that memory or these memories up on a TV screen on a wall, and for the moment let the screen go blank.

Instruction: If no particular memory comes to mind, repeat last paragraph, 'Ask yourself, "When have I felt like this before"...' etc., until a memory arises, then proceed. If, after asking several times no memory arises, proceed to the next phase and (unless a memory subsequently reveals itself at the campfire) eliminate the Change Memory section.

Campfire

Now imagine that you and your mentor are sitting by a campfire right here ... right where you are in this organ or tissue. The nature of this campfire is unconditional love, openness, pure being ... Source itself ... You and your mentor are filled with pure freedom as you sit here by this fire ... And now you can bring to the fire the specific people who are involved with the old issues around the patterns of depression... All those who are associated with this old series of reactions ...Who needs to be here at the fire?... Who should be here?... [Let answer]... Okay, great... Do any other people need to be at this campfire?... [Let answer]... Great.

So... can you see the campfire?... Can you see the younger you?... The present you? ... The mentor?... Who else is here?... [Let answer. Write down names]

Of the people involved with this issue, and in the knowledge that anyone else there will hear what needs to be heard... to whom would you like to speak first?... [Let answer]

Instruction: Go through ALL points 1-11 for EACH person spoken to, i.e., recycle through points 1-11 if a second person is addressed

1. So everyone is sitting in the protective presence of this fire of unconditional love and acceptance. The younger you may have experienced a great deal of pain in the past. Now let the younger you speak from that previous pain, saying what needs to be said, and let_____ [Name of person spoken to] hear what needs to be heard... [Let answer]

2. Knowing that_____ was probably doing the best he/she could with the resources he/she had at the time, let him/her reply... [Let answer]

3. What does the younger you have to reply?... [Let answer]

4. If_____ [Name] was to reply, not from the level of the personality but from the level of the soul, what might he/she say?... [Let answer]

5. What does the younger you have to reply to that?... [Let conversation continue both ways until completely emptied out, then continue]

6. What advice might the mentor have to add?... [Let answer]

7. What does the present you have to say to_____ [Name]?... [Let answer]

8. What would_____ [Name] reply from the level of the soul?... [Let answer]

9. *Does anyone have anything more to add?... [Continue until empty]*

10. *When the younger you is ready, ask: "Even though his/her previous behavior may not have been acceptable by any standards... even if you in no way condone his/her behavior, are you willing to completely and utterly forgive him/her from the bottom of your heart?... [Let answer]... Now go ahead and forgive him/her... [Let forgive]*

11. *When the present you is ready, ask: "Even though his/her previous behavior may not have been acceptable by any standards; even if you in no way condone his/her behavior, are you willing to completely and utterly forgive him/her from the bottom of your heart?... [Let answer]... Now go ahead and forgive him/her... [Let forgive]... Good.*

Beliefs Change

Now turn to the mentor and begin to explore what unhealthy beliefs have been here in the past. What beliefs have you inherited, or bought into that are unsupportive and inappropriate?... Particularly those beliefs around patterns of depression and emotional shut down, collapse or resistance... Any old beliefs around who or how you needed to be in order to survive, or be safe, or to avoid getting hurt... Or old beliefs about life's struggles and pains... What unsupportive beliefs did you inherit or come to believe? Just empty them all out... [Let answer. Give time and encouragement. Write down old beliefs]

Now, just ask the mentor to sweep your body and your being clean of all these old beliefs... And as I read them all out... Just allow the mentor to use all possible tools to sweep them, wash them, clear them from all consciousness... [Read out old beliefs]... letting the mentor wash and clean and sweep and scrub all that old consciousness out of every part of your being ... cleansing and purifying... completely removing that old stuff... from your cells... from your molecules... from your DNA... from the spaces between the spaces... right down to the level of consciousness itself... Let it all be purged and purified... And just make sure the mentor gets into all the stuck places... and the dark places... and the secret places... until the job is totally and finally done... And you can let me know when that is completely complete... Just take as much time as it needs in order to be totally and completely finished... [Give sufficient time]...

Fabulous!... Now just ask the mentor of freedom: What is the deepest truth, the real truth? What is the deepest understanding that can be accessed about life and living it healthily and fully? And if there were words of truth, of deepest realization that could be installed in place of those old beliefs... What truths would be installed?... Just let the words flow... [Let answer. Give time. Be encouraging]... Great.

And now just let the mentor install these truths, these realizations into every particle of your being ... into every fiber of your being... Let the mentor upload this certitude, this deepest understanding into every cell... every molecule... into your DNA... into the spaces between the spaces... flooding all of consciousness with this deepest revelation... this deepest truth... You can take as much time as it takes for this to be completely complete... Just let me know when it's finally done... [Give sufficient time]... Fabulous!

And just rest and bask in the consciousness of these new realizations... Feeling how healing and liberating it is to be reprogrammed with your own deepest realization... as we move on in the process.

Change Memory

And now, just bring back in your mind's eye the TV screen that you put the memory or memories up on a short while ago... Can you see the screen, or just get a sense or knowing that it's there?... Great.

> **Instruction: If no memory was elicited eliminate the Change Memory and go directly to the Self-forgiveness section.**

And now as you sit by the campfire, in the protective presence of the mentor of freedom, getting ready to view the scene or series of scenes being played on the movie screen... When you are ready, go ahead and play the scene, and when it's over, let the screen go blank and let me know... [Give sufficient time]... Please describe to me what took place in the scene... [Let answer]... Now have the younger you step down off the screen and come over to the campfire and sit with the present you and the mentor.

*Now as you all sit peacefully at this fire, ask the present you or your mentor what kinds of resourceful states you **would** have found useful in the scene... [Give time to come up with resourceful states. Be encouraging. Let partner name them. Write them down]...*

Now let the younger you in the scene receive a huge bouquet of balloons containing all these resourceful states or emotions. As you receive each balloon breathe in the quality or resource in the balloon. Now put the scene up on the movie screen and see how it would have happened if you'd had access to all these resourceful states... When it's over let the screen go blank and let me know... [Give sufficient time]... How did it play out?... Just give me a brief description... [Let answer]... Good.

Now just let the younger you and the other people in the scene step down off the screen and come back to the campfire... and, turning to those present at the fire, go ahead and forgive them all... sending them blessings... Allow them to merge into the fire, which is the source of all life...

Self-forgiveness

Now turn to the younger you and say: "I forgive you for any previous pain which was caused; you just didn't have access to the resources that I do now, and now you can have access to them any time you like. I promise you will never have to experience this previous pain again, because I love you and will always protect you."

Then, hugging the younger you, let yourself merge, allowing the younger you to grow up with this forgiveness and these resources inside.

And now, either you or the mentor can cut any unhealthy energetic ties, umbilical cords or binding strings with those you have forgiven... making sure that Source or light is sent down both ends of the cords as they are cut... and you can let me know when that's complete... [Give sufficient time]... Great.

Return to Present Moment Consciousness

Now, let the campfire disappear ... Only you and your mentor are left... take out your high-beam flashlights and shine them all around... What do you see?... How are things changing?... [Let answer]... Great... Is there any final communication the organ or tissue itself wants to make?... [Give time]... Great.

And knowing that the body and being will continue to heal perfectly, automatically, of its own accord, and that this forgiveness and realization can only deepen over time... and knowing that the part of you responsible for making your heart beat and your eyes shine and your cells replicate will continue the healing process perfectly, without you even thinking about it, the way it does all the time, quite naturally while you are sleeping... you and your mentor can leave with grateful hearts.

And having completed your process for today, it's time to get back into your space shuttle and let it take you and your mentor back to the doorway you came through... Now step outside the shuttle and thank your mentor with all your heart ... Now walk through the doorway and over to the staircase you first came down.

Now, step onto step 1... and as we count back from 1 to 10 you will feel yourself becoming more refreshed, alive and joyous... 2... 3... awake to your own innate freedom and greatness... 4... you can stretch and let your body feel more energized... 5... 6... 7... becoming focused, refreshed, ready to wake up to the full potential of your own infinite presence... free in your own openness, power and beauty... 8... feeling alive, fully expressed, fully potentialized as the full energy of life itself... 9... and you may open your eyes ONLY as soon as all parts of you are fully integrated and ready to continue the process naturally on its own... and 10... you may open your eyes now, when you're ready... Well done...

Great work!

Please now allow a little quiet time so the results of this process can begin to integrate. You may feel some temporary shakiness, wooziness or slight disorientation as your body adjusts to the emotional and physical shift that has just taken place - this is absolutely normal, and in fact is a positive signal that healing is happening. These effects will pass of their own accord, normally within an hour to a few hours, so there is nothing specific that you need to do. Just relax and let things resolve naturally, automatically. You can support yourself while this takes place by getting some rest and eating easily digestible food - something plain and simple and soothing - and maybe by taking a warm bath or shower. Then your body can focus on what it knows how to do: healing.

And when this re-adjustment is complete you will likely feel as if something deep has shifted, like a weight has been lifted or a tension released internally. These, again, are positive signs that transformation has taken place.

Give yourself some time, preferably at least 24 hours, before undergoing the next introspection. Then please keep going. You are making good progress and there is a little way to go yet.

Instructions: The Gentle Welcome and The Emotional Journey Process

Download the audio and script at www.kevinbillett.org/book-bonus

Intention:
That you allow your emotions to be fully felt and deepen, allowing increasingly deep emotions to be experienced until you open into your essence, Source. Then to verbally empty out any words associated with an old hurt or trauma, forgive and resolve that old issue.

Time:
60 to 90 minutes

Emotional level:
Emotional to deeply emotional

What you need:
Pen/paper, tissues

At the end:
Short break of 30 minutes or so.

The Emotional Journey Process is the cornerstone of all Journeywork. Like the Physical Journey, it is one of the original Journey introspections and has helped huge numbers of people from countries all over the world to transform their lives, their core life experience, and enjoy a sense of freedom, peace and joy that few could have imagined. This version of the Emotional Journey has been adapted specifically for use with depression, and is a slightly simpler, more streamlined version of the introspection previously published in other Journey books.

The process requires us to open with a starting emotion, something we currently access and feel strongly. To access a strong emotion simply stop, sit, close your eyes, look down inside your body and remember a time when you did feel a strong emotion, a time when you were really triggered.

If no strong emotion is apparent or accessible, you can use the Emotional Gentle Welcome process below to access an emotion before moving on to the main part of the process, and if you can access and feel something relatively potent as you go into the process you can skip the Emotional Gentle Welcome and go straight into the Emotional Journey, using the emotion you are feeling as the starting point.

The script reader should proceed at a pace comfortable for the partner undergoing the work, and if there is any doubt about pacing can just ask if the speed is ok or if it needs slowing down or speeding up. The reader can also help the process by being willing to open empathetically, to be emotionally 'in tune' with the one with closed eyes so that the reading can reflect that rapport.

The script then invites us to welcome the emotions that reveal themselves and feel them fully, as we are guided into deeper and deeper emotions. It is a bit like an emotional unveiling, or like uncovering a pancake stack of emotions as we progressively 'drop through' each emotional layer and eventually open into spacious awareness, our essence, Source. It is here, deeper than the thinking mind, while resting in spacious presence that some profound healing work can take place.

If, while opening and dropping through the various emotional layers you encounter layers like, 'stuck', 'nothing' or 'void', or 'blackness' please just treat them as if they were another emotional layer and keep gently asking 'What's deeper than this?' or 'What is in the heart of this?' And if you just relax and go with the script it will work just fine.

If you are in doubt as to what needs to take place at the campfire, simply ask the mentor, 'What needs to happen (right here at this campfire) so this issue can be complete and healed?' And if, when forgiveness is asked for, it is slow or difficult, in similar fashion you can ask the mentor, 'What needs to happen (right here at this campfire) so forgiveness can happen?'

The mentor is, please remember, a profoundly wise resource capable of answering any question from deepest truth, absolute freedom. And you can access that wisdom at any point after you have welcomed the presence of a mentor.

Whenever you see "..." the reader should pause and give their partner sufficient time to fully experience the pure, raw emotion or to let the question sink in deeply before answering. The pauses may often be very short. Once they have experienced it fully move on. Start with your partner's strongest emotional issue or response to the eliciting question, and repeat the highlighted section immediately below to guide your partner down through the emotional levels and into Source.

The Emotional Journey process usually takes around an hour to an hour-and-a-half, and it is wise to take a little relaxation time immediately afterwards, so please make sure you allow sufficient time to relax and be spacious as you process. Have a wonderful Emotional Journey.

Instruction: The Gentle Welcome Process

Download the audio and script at www.kevinbillett.org/book-bonus

Intention:
That you gently tune into your body to discover what emotions you may be feeling at a deeper level. That you use the strongest emotion you discover as a starting point for the next exercise, The Emotional Journey process

Time:
10 to 15 minutes

Emotional level:
Emotional to deeply emotional

What you need:
Quiet space. Pen and paper. Tissues

At the end:
Move directly on to The Emotional Journey Process

Emotional Gentle Welcome Process

If you are already experiencing a strong emotion, feel free to skip The Gentle Welcome Process and go straight to The Emotional Journey Process. The Gentle Welcome Process is optional and is designed to elicit a strong emotion, when one is not already being felt. Keep reading The Gentle Welcome only until a strong emotion is experienced. Once a strong emotion is felt, stop with The Gentle Welcome and go straight into The Emotional Journey Process, which follows immediately after.

Exercise 8: The Gentle Welcome Process

Sometimes we all have a little difficulty feeling our emotions. It's natural. So let's take a few moments to turn within, to open and experience what is here. So you can gently

close your eyes, take a few deep breaths in... and out... and just let your body soften, open and relax... Softening your face... relaxing the corners of the mouth... relaxing the jaw... softening the throat... relaxing the shoulders... softening the chest... opening the door to your own heart as you relax and soften your belly... soften your pelvic region... your thighs, legs... Just let your whole body relax and open.

Now let your awareness become spacious, letting your heart be as wide as the world... let it become vast in front of you... boundless behind... infinite to all sides... and just rest as an open sky of all acceptance... And into this vast sky of acceptance welcome all of your emotions... all the feelings you have ever felt... even your ancestors' emotions... your love is so vast that it is big and open enough to welcome them all...

Now turn your awareness inside the body. Your body, your being, is like a container, a vessel full of all kinds of emotions, all kinds of feelings and our feelings, they are like little kids... some are loud and attention seeking, some quiet and shy, still others have hidden themselves away beneath lids or behind closed doors... They may not trust you yet because they have been rejected so many times... so you might like to apologize to your feelings and let them know that for once you are going to be open, you are going to listen and be present to feel whatever is arising.

And now find an area of your body that might be a little tense, contracted or held in some way... and just breathe into that area, flooding it with your own love, your own acceptance, letting it soften and open... and if there were an emotion there, I wonder what it might be... Some of our feelings are very subtle, so just welcome whatever is here...

Or perhaps there isn't a feeling, but rather a picture arising. If that's the case, then how does the picture make you feel?... Or if this area could speak and had words, what might it be saying?... [Let answer]... How does that make you feel?... [Let answer]... Just welcome whatever is here and also whatever is not here. [Let them name an emotion and then say]... Where in the body does that feeling grab you most strongly?... Where in your body do you feel it most?... [Let answer. Write down emotion and where in body]... Just allow this emotion to become even fuller... [Encourage to feel fully]... Now let yourself come to neutral and find another area where there might be a little tension, stress, holding or hiding going on... Once again flood it with your own love, your own acceptance... And if there were a feeling beginning to arise right now, what might that feeling be?... [Give time. Let answer]... Or if there were words, what might it be saying?... [Let answer]... How do those words make you feel?... [Let answer]... Or if there was a picture, how does this picture make you feel?... Or perhaps there is a lid or a door. If there is a lid, just feel yourself peeling the lid back and ask, 'What am I covering? What am I hiding from?'... and just open into whatever emotion has shown up... How does that make you feel?... [Give time. Let answer and write down]... Where is it arising most strongly?... [Let answer and write down]... And just allow it to be even fuller... [Give time. Encourage to feel more fully]... Thank you... And now come to neutral...

And now find a third area where there might be some tension, contraction or holding going on. Breathe into that area... Let it be suffused with your own acceptance... If an emotion were arising here, what might it be?... [Let answer]... Or if it had words, what might it say?... [Let answer]... Or if there is a picture, then how does it make you feel?... [Let answer]... Just welcome whatever is here and whatever is not here... Perhaps there might even be a door here... If so, just open the door... What's hiding behind there... and how does it make you feel?... [Give time. Let answer and write down]... Where do you feel it most strongly?... [Let answer and write down]... You can even allow it to become even fuller now...

Now... of these three emotions, which is strongest for you? [Give time. Let name emotion.]

Note: This strongest emotion is the starting point for the Emotional Journey. Ask your partner to keep their eyes closed and to keep feeling this emotion. Then move on to The Emotional Journey script.

Exercise 9

Instructions: The Emotional Journey Process

Download the audio and script at www.kevinbillett.org/book-bonus

Your partner should be sitting comfortably with eyes closed. If you have used The Gentle Welcome Process, start with the strongest emotion your partner uncovered. Otherwise, to directly access a strong emotion, ask them with eyes closed, to look down inside their body and sense into what they are really feeling. Once they have accessed a strong, or reasonably strong emotion, you can continue reading below. Make sure your parter names the feeling at every level.

Intention:
That you allow your emotions to be fully felt and deepen, allowing increasingly deep emotions to be experienced until you open in your essence, Source. Then that you verbally empty out any words associated with an old hurt or trauma, and forgive and resolve that issue.
Time:
60 to 90 minutes
Emotional level:
Emotional to deeply emotional
What you need:
Quiet space. Pen and paper. Tissues
At the end:
Break of 30 minutes or so

Exercise 9: The Emotional Journey Process

Bring all awareness to this feeling and just let it grow... Open and welcome it fully...

Where in your body is this emotion strongest? Where do you feel it?

Just allow all the feeling to come flooding... Really welcome it... As you let the feeling grow stronger... ask yourself... What's beneath this?... What's in the core of it?... And feel yourself relaxing and opening right into it... Welcoming it all...

Just open into or drop into whatever is beneath... (It may not be what you are expecting, so just stay open and let it reveal itself now)...

So, what are you feeling?...

Great... thank you...

Note: Keep repeating the highlighted sections above, dropping through to the next level and the next until your partner opens into Source, essence. The non-highlighted section in parentheses is optional; use it occasionally. Once in Source, reassure your partner, tell them they are doing a great job and let them rest here for approximately 15 to 30 seconds, then continue with the Campfire. Source may be called many names, and will be boundary-less. It will have a vast quality such as absolute freedom; silence; unlimited peace; eternal; eternity; God; unlimited love; unconditional love; boundlessness; all that is; consciousness; pure being; awareness; emptiness; vastness, etc. It is normally experienced inside and outside the body, or in an 'everywhere and nowhere' way that makes it unlocatable, omnipresent.

Campfire

*Imagine a campfire... the nature of which is vast boundlessness, unconditional love and absolute freedom. Imagine a **younger you** sitting at this fire... Now picture the **present you** sitting at the fire... Also at this fire is a **mentor** whose wisdom you trust - it can be someone you know or would like to know... a saint, a sage, or someone born of your imagination... someone in whose divine presence you feel safe, and whose views on life and living it fully are free, expansive and wise... Now bring to the fire the specific people who are involved with your issue... Regarding any limiting memories or beliefs around depression, or closing to or resisting life, who else should be at this campfire?... [Give time. Let answer]*

*Can you see the campfire?... Can you see the **younger you**?... The **present you**?... The **mentor**?... Who else is here?... [Let answer. Write down names so you can refer to them specifically, i.e. mother, father, loved one, teacher, etc.]... Of the people involved with your issue, to which **one or two** would you like to speak? [Let answer]... Good... And to whom would you like to speak first?...*

Instruction: Go through all points 1-13 for each person spoken to, i.e., recycle through points 1-13 if a second person is addressed

1. *Everyone is now sitting in the protective presence of this fire of unconditional love, acceptance and freedom. The **younger you** may have experienced a great deal of pain in the past that resulted in some shutting down or some resistance. Let the **younger you** speak now from that previous pain, saying what **really** needs to be said, and letting _____ [Name of person spoken to] hear what **really** needs to be heard ... [Let answer fully]*

2. *Knowing that _____ was probably doing the best they could with the resources they had at the time, let them reply out loud... [Let answer]*

3. *Does the **younger you** have anything to reply to that?... [Let answer fully]*

4. *If _____ were to reply, not from the level of the personality, but from a deeper level, what might they say?... [Let answer]*

5. *Does the **younger you** have anything to reply to that?... [Let answer fully and keep emptying out in this way until fully empty. When everything that needs to be said has been said, continue]*

6. *Does the mentor have anything to add?... [Let answer]*

7. *What does the present you have to say to _____?... [Let answer fully]*

8. *What would _____ reply from a deeper level?... [Let answer fully]*

9. *Does anyone have anything more to add?... [Let answer. Keep emptying out in this way until empty, then continue with Change Memory section]*

Change Memory

Instruction: Elicit each individual memory

10. *What memories come to mind where you have felt shut down in some way to life, to circumstances or to your own emotions... when you hid or put on a blanket or covering to protect you? Are there times that you held back and played small, or began closing down to life itself? ... Are there memories of others' negativity undermining you or hurting you? ... Or are there times when, to avoid your real feelings, you blanked them or blocked them out?... Just let me know what memories of this type you recall...*

Instruction: Be encouraging. Get partner to describe each memory fully, then write down a word or short phrase of reference to describe each one

Great... Thank you... So now put these memories up on a screen on the wall, and let them play out to the end, the way they played out at that time... Allow each one to complete, and then let the screen go blank and just nod your head to let me know when it is done... [Give time]... Great...

Now, as you sit peacefully at this fire, ask yourself or your mentor what kind of internal resources you **could** *have used which would have been helpful at that time ... [Give time to come up with resourceful states. Be encouraging and suggest empowering qualities as necessary]*

Now go ahead and put these resources into a balloon bouquet and hand them to the younger you letting the younger you breathe in these qualities, letting them suffuse the whole body. Now let the younger you step back onto the screen and see and experience the way the scene **would** *have happened if you'd had access to these resources at that time... [Give time]...*

So what happened this time?... How was it different?... [Let answer]...

> **Instruction: Use the same balloons for each memory, playing them anew, one at a time, from this empowered experience. When all memories have been replayed, continue below.**

Now let the younger you step down from the screen and rejoin you at the campfire.

Belief Elicitation and Sweep-clean

11. Now come back to the campfire and ask yourself: if there were some unhealthy beliefs that you picked up along the way, what might they be? Sometimes we absorb disempowering beliefs, ideas, and concepts through people's actions, words, society's conditioning or through our own experience. If there were any remaining unhealthy views on life and living it fully, what might they be?

> **Instruction: Write down each disempowering belief, then, once the list is complete, repeat each one briefly to your partner before moving on**

And now just ask the mentor to step inside the body of the younger you and sweep you completely clean of these old limiting beliefs, and any other unhealthy beliefs that may be present. Let the mentor sweep them out, wash them out, vacuum them out... whichever is appropriate... Just experience how it feels as a complete spring-clean of those old issues takes place... And make sure the mentor gets into all the dark corners and hidden or secret places... cleaning everything out at a cellular level... right into the core of your cells... into the DNA itself... and even deeper, right down to the level of consciousness... to the spaces between the spaces... [Give time]... And when this feels absolutely complete you can let me know by nodding your head... [Give plenty of time]... Great!

Now, if the mentor were to speak from the place of absolute freedom and could suggest some supportive, empowering and integrative truths that would allow you to live in a more empowered and free way, what would the mentor suggest?... [Read old and then elicit new and empowering truths as antidotes. Give time. Let answer]... Great!... So just allow the mentor to install these new, healthy truths into every cell of the body... Just experience how it feels as the mentor infuses every fiber of your being with these brand new, wholesome realizations... drenching, filling, renewing all of consciousness with positivity and health...

And when this is complete you can let me know [Give sufficient time]... Fabulous!... Thank you.

Final Forgiveness

12. Now, having experienced such a deep sweep-clean, a clear out on all levels and having learned what you have learned, ask the **younger you** to speak to the person at the campfire... and even though this person's previous beliefs may have been very disempowering... and even though their previous behavior may not have been acceptable by **any** standards... and even if you in no way condone their behavior or beliefs, are you willing to **completely and utterly** forgive them?... Now go ahead and forgive them from the bottom of your heart ... [Let them voice forgiveness out loud]

13. When the **present you** is ready now... even though this person's previous behavior may not have been acceptable by **any** standards, and even if you in no way condone their behavior or beliefs, are you willing to **completely and utterly** forgive them from the bottom of your heart?"... Now go ahead and forgive them... [Let voice forgiveness out loud]... You can even make a prayer that somehow they will find self-forgiveness.

Go ahead and forgive all those at the campfire, sending them blessings. Allow them to merge into the fire, which is the infinite source of all life. Then turn to the **younger you** and say: "I promise you will never have to experience this again. I forgive you for any pain that was caused, and for not having access to these expanded realizations at that time, and you can always have access to them any time now. I love you and will always protect you."... Then hugging the **younger you**, let yourself merge, become one, allowing the **younger you** to grow up inside the body of the **present you** with this forgiveness, this completion and all these internal resources inside... *[Give time]*... Turning to the **mentor**, thank him/her... Now come back to the present and we will continue. Allow awareness to expand spaciously in front, vastly behind and openly to all sides, opening as an ocean of presence.

Future Integration

Having learned what you've learned, having experienced what you've experienced, open into the consciousness of you a day from now... feel how you are feeling... breathe how you are breathing... How are you feeling?... Knowing that you are _____ [Source], imagine a situation arising that would have triggered your old issue around depression. What does _____ [Source] say to it?... See how you are handling it now... What kind of things are you doing?... Saying?... Feeling?... How do you feel about yourself?

Now see yourself a week from now... open into the consciousness... feel how you are feeling... breathe how you are breathing... How are you feeling?... Imagine some old issue appearing... What does _____ [Source] say to it?... How are you handling it?... What do you look like?... What kind of things are you saying to yourself?... What kinds of actions are you taking?... How are you feeling?...

Step into the future a month from now and open into the consciousness, feel how you are feeling, breathe how you are breathing, how are you feeling?... What if that old situation was to arise?... How are you handling it? What does _____ [Source] say to it?... Are you feeling free, confident and light?... What are you saying to yourself?... What are you doing?... How does your body feel?...

Now open into the consciousness of you six months down the line. How are you feeling, about yourself, about freedom, about life in general?...

Now step into the future a whole year from now, getting a full sense of how it feels to be you, to be alive and thriving as you are... Breathe how you are breathing a year from now... and feel how you are feeling... What are you feeling?... Are any of the old issues arising, or are you feeling free, healthy and on purpose?... And if one of the old triggers of depression were to show up in life, how differently would you respond now?... Is handling things a breeze?... Great...

Now step into the future five years from now... open into the consciousness of you five years down the line... Feel how you are feeling... What are you doing differently these days?... How are you communicating differently... to yourself... and to others?... How *does your body feel?... How are you feeling about yourself... your life... the future?...*

*Now, staying connected to the future you, **to the source of you five years from now**... breathing that way... feeling that way... your cells vibrating at that enhanced level... just ask the future you to give some advice to the present you. Let the free, wise future you ten years from now, share some words of wisdom on how to be ... what to believe ... giving practical advice on what to do to revel in your new life... how to stay open, connected, alive... free ... [Give time. Let answer]... Great, thank you...*

So, knowing that you will only be able to open your eyes as soon as all parts of you are completely integrated and agreed that the realization, the freedom, the health that is here can only grow and deepen over time, and when all parts of you are agreed that this can take place perfectly, naturally of its own accord, effortlessly and gracefully, then you can softly open your eyes now, when you are ready.

Great job! Beautiful process... Congratulations!

As with the Physical Journey, please now allow a little quiet time so the results of this process can begin to integrate. You may feel some temporary shakiness, wooziness or slight disorientation as your body adjusts to the emotional and physical shift that has just taken place - remember, this is absolutely normal, and in fact is a positive signal that transformation is happening. These effects will pass of their own accord, normally within an hour to a few hours, so there is nothing specific that you need to do. Just relax and let things resolve naturally, automatically. You can support yourself while this takes place by getting some rest and eating easily digestible food - something plain and simple and soothing - and maybe by taking a warm bath or shower. Then your body can focus on what it knows how to do: healing.

And when this re-adjustment is complete you will likely feel as if something deep has shifted, like a weight has been lifted or a tension released internally. These, again, are positive signs that significant shift has taken place.

Give yourself some time, preferably at least 24 hours, before undergoing the next introspection. Then please keep going. You are making great progress and there is still some work to do.

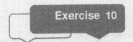

Instructions: The Worst-Best Journey Process

Download the audio and script at www.kevinbillett.org/book-bonus

Intention:

That you allow some fears to surface and your emotions to be fully felt and deepen, allowing increasingly deep emotions to be experienced until you open in your essence, Source. Then to verbally empty out any words associated with an old hurt or trauma, and forgive and resolve that issue.

Time:

60 to 90 minutes

Emotional level:

Emotional to deeply emotional

What you need:

Quiet space. Pen and paper. Tissues

At the end:

Break of 30 minutes or so

This guided introspection is similar in structure to the Emotional Journey, and it has many common elements, including a drop through and a campfire. There are also some differences.

The drop through technique is different, and we will ask what is the worst that could happen if depression was no longer available as a protective 'blanket'… that might seem like a strange question, but it ultimately makes a lot of sense if we simply see that the habit of depression would not exist unless it gave us some sort of perceived benefits. Those benefits may be as simple as providing emotional protection so we don't have to face or feel some sharp or raw emotions, and there may also be different, unexpected benefits.

So here we will be asking for a 'worst case scenario' at each level, and noting how that makes us feel emotionally as we open deeper and deeper, eventually into Source. Many people find this easier and quicker than a regular emotional drop through. And in any case this technique will allow us to uncover and feel some of the emotions that depression might have been protecting us from, so we can experience first hand that even these emotions are safe to feel, safe to open completely with.

A second difference in this process is an added technique that we will employ to change our unhealthy beliefs. At the campfire, working with the understanding that throughout life we tend to cover over our older beliefs with layers of new beliefs we will do a Beliefs Drop Through as well as a Beliefs Change. A Beliefs Drop Through simply means that we will enquire what beliefs might be deeper than the one being experienced, and deeper than that, and so on. Eventually we will come to a core or foundational belief, one that is the deepest of the deep. Then, in similar style to the question we started this whole process with, we will ask what would happen, what would be felt emotionally, if this core, foundational belief were no longer available to us. And we will quickly open with that emotion and go into the heart, and into the heart of it until we open again into Source. Then we will continue with the regular Beliefs Change that you are already familiar with.

This is a deeply clearing addition to the process, and it is easy, so just relax and follow the script. Most other elements of the process will already be familiar to you, until you get about half way through the Future Integration at the end of the introspection. There you will find a slight change in that we will begin to ask from the fresh transformed consciousness being experienced, what's the best, the very best that could now happen. Then it is time to get enthusiastic, excited about the new possibilities life has to offer.

Please make sure to allow sufficient time to go through this process thoroughly and have some relaxing, integrative time afterwards.

Go for it, and have a powerful Worst-Best clear out.

Exercise 10: The Worst-Best Journey Process

> Note: If at any time a memory shows up, just make a note in your notebook and bring that memory to the campfire.

If you could no longer rely on the 'blanket' of depression... the suppression, shutting down or deflation of your emotions, physicality or mind... to protect you from what you are really feeling or facing at a deeper level... If you had to be fully open, exposed and authentic in life from now onwards...

What's the worst that could happen?... [Let answer]... And if that were fully welcomed here... How does that really make you feel?... [Let reply]

Just allow all the feeling to come flooding... Open and welcome all of it... And as you let the feeling grow stronger... ask ...

Then what's the worst that could happen?...

How does that really make you feel?... Really welcome all of it...

And if that happened, what's the very worst that could happen?...

And how does that really make you feel?...

> Note: Continue by repeating the underlined section immediately above starting, "Then what's the worst..." etc. Repeat these questions, encouraging your partner to open deeper until openness, emptiness, spaciousness or a positive nothingness - inside, outside, everywhere - is experienced. Then continue with section beneath.

Just open into the heart of it... Just relax and expand into it... What's here?... What reveals itself?... And just open into the heart of that... relax and expand into the essence of it... What reveals itself?... What is here?... [Let answer]

Instruction: Repeat underlined section above, opening and expanding into the heart of each experience until Source, infinite or boundless awareness, stillness, clarity, realization, consciousness, presence, etc., is experienced. Then continue beneath

*And just rest **as** this for a short while...*

Campfire

Now, imagine a campfire... the nature of which is boundless truth, freedom. Imagine a **younger you** sitting at this fire... Now picture the **present you** sitting at the fire... Also at this fire is a **mentor of freedom, of enlightened presence**... one in whose infinite wisdom you can rest and trust... And now ask, who else needs to be at this campfire?... Who should be here? [Let answer. Encourage. Reference anyone who showed up during drop through, and anyone who is related to any memory that showed up, and welcome them to the campfire.]

And as we sit in the presence of this campfire of love and freedom, just know that if anyone else needs to be welcomed at any time, that can just happen automatically as we now focus on opening into sharing some truths that need to be spoken... So, of the people present here at the campfire, to which **one or two** would you like to speak?... And to whom would you like to speak first?...

> Note: Go through all points 1-8 with each person to be spoken to. At all stages encourage your partner to speak and empty out *from* the heart of the emotional pain that was or is felt: not *about* the emotions, but *from* the emotions.

1. With everyone embraced by a protective presence at this fire of absolute freedom, and knowing that the **younger you** may have experienced a great deal of pain in the past around the issue of authenticity, exposure and truth... just let the **younger you** speak now from that previous pain, saying what **really** needs to be said, and letting _____ [Name of person spoken to] hear what **really** needs to be heard... [Let answer]

2. Knowing that _____ [Name] was probably doing the best they could with the resources they had at the time, let them reply from their heart... [Let answer]

3. And what does the **younger you** have to reply to that?... [Let answer fully]

4. If _____ [Name] were to reply, not from the level of the personality, but from a deeper level, what might they say?... [Let answer]

5. And from the deepest level, what does the **younger you** reply to that? ... [Let answer fully. Keep emptying out in this way until completely empty. When all are empty continue below.]

6. And if the **mentor** had something to add, what might that be? What wisdom or advice or realization might the mentor share... [Let answer]

7. *Does anyone have anything more to add?... [Let answer. Keep emptying out in this way until completely empty, then continue on to Change Memory Process.]*

Change Memory Process

8. *Imagine a big movie screen at the campfire of infinite freedom. And invite into consciousness any old memories where the younger you felt triggered into shut down or emotional blocking... some time when you reacted by collapsing, emotionally or energetically... or when you felt overwhelmed or diminished by life... What memories begin to arise?... [Give time]... Great... What specifically took place?... What else took place?... What else?... Thank you.*

> Note: Be encouraging, get partner to describe each memory fully, then write down a word or short phrase of reference to describe each memory. Also refer to any memory that was uncovered during the drop-through phase, which you should have written down.

*Now, invite the younger you down off the screen to sit at this fire, with you and your mentor and ask yourself what kind of internal resources you **could** have used which would have been helpful at that time... [Give time to come up with resourceful states. Be encouraging and suggest empowering qualities. Write down so you can read them back]*

*Now go ahead and put these resources into a balloon bouquet and hand them to the younger you letting the younger you breathe in these qualities, letting them suffuse the whole body. Now let the younger you step back onto the screen and see and experience the way they **would** have happened if you'd had access to these resources at that time... [Give sufficient time]*

So what happened this time?... How was it different? ... [Let answer]

> Note: Use the same resource balloons for each memory, playing them anew, individually, from this empowered experience.

Now let the younger you step down from the screen and re-join you at the campfire.

> Note: Ask partner if she/he needs to speak to a second person at the campfire. If so, go back to points 1-8, emptying out and coming to forgiveness with second person. Then move on to point 9.

Beliefs Elicitation, Drop-Through & Clear-Out

9. Now, as awareness comes back to the campfire, ask the younger you, if there were some unhealthy or unsupportive beliefs about emotions, about openness or exposure, or about life itself that you picked some time ago, what might they be? Maybe there are some beliefs about how you needed to react, or how you needed to behave in order to survive... Or maybe they are old beliefs about depression and what it means to be depressed... If so, what old beliefs might they be?...

We can absorb disempowering beliefs, ideas, and concepts through people's actions or words, through society's expectations or through our own experience of life's traumas. If there were any remaining unhealthy views about being free to live life as an expression of your real self, what might they be? [Write down each disempowering belief]

And if there were a **deeper belief** than these, what might be here? What's deeper than this?...

And if that belief relied on another, **even deeper, belief**... what might be here? What's underneath this?

> Note: Keep eliciting deeper and deeper beliefs, by repeating the question above, dropping through to core belief or emotion.

And if there was a **belief underneath all other unhealthy beliefs** ... or **right at the core of all other beliefs**... what might that be?... If there was a **prime, foundational belief** that shored up all the others... what could that be?... [Let answer]... And how does it really feel to contemplate or admit that belief?... What does it bring up for you emotionally... at the deepest level? [Let answer]... Great.

And if you could no longer hold on to this foundational belief... if you could no longer rely on it to protect you emotionally ... what would you really feel?... If someone came and stole away your ability to rely on this belief... pulled the rug on it... what would you risk feeling emotionally, at the very deepest level?... Great... So just free fall into this emotion, and surrender to it completely, no matter what.

Keep letting go into the heart of this until it is done with you... Just keep opening into it, as it grows more and more intense... Let go completely until it decides to finish with you... [Give time]... Wonderful... And what is here... right in the heart, the essence?... Great job.

> Note: Keep opening into the heart of what shows up. Open freshly into expansiveness, Source, infinite awareness, then gently proceed.

So, now bring your awareness back to campfire... and **welcome a representative of all these old, restricting beliefs***... someone or something that represents or embodies the whole consciousness of those old beliefs...*

And in the realization that all the old beliefs were put in place and maintained in the mistaken belief that they would bring you specific benefits... maybe protect you in some emotional, physical or mental way... Now let the younger you dialogue with the **beliefs representative***... asking what its positive intent was... staying open to hear the support that was intended... [Give time. Encourage]... So what were the supposed benefits?... [Give time. Encourage]*

And what mistake was made?... [Let answer]... What were some of the results of that mistake, or mistaken belief?... What price did you pay? What did it cost you to believe what you used to believe?... [Let answer]... And what is the deeper, more authentic truth?... What is the absolute truth... [Let answer]

Now let the younger you empty out completely with the beliefs representative... expressing anything that needs to be expressed... anything that has previously remained suppressed or contained... Just speak it all out from your heart of hearts... [Give time. Encourage]

And if the beliefs representative could respond from its true purpose... What might be said?... [Give time. Encourage]

> Note: Continue dialogue with beliefs representative until empty, then allow forgiveness in both directions.

And if the mentor had any words of wisdom or advice for you, what would be shared? [Let mentor speak]

And now just invite the mentor to clear, to cleanse, to pull out all the old beliefs and allow them to merge into the light of infinite awareness... watching and feeling as they leave the physical body... and the mind... withdrawing them all from head to toe... from the brain... and the head... from the heart and the chest... and the arms... and legs... from the stuck, or secret, or dark places... from the cells... from the DNA... from the spaces between the spaces... Take as much time as is needed... [Give plenty of time. Gently encourage]... And you can nod when you are ready to let me know when that feels totally complete... [Give time]... Great...

Now just notice what happens when the energy that was previously needed to hold these old beliefs in place is released... and becomes available to you right now... It took a whole load of energy and closure to hold onto those unsupportive beliefs... So, how does it feel to have all this openness released... to have an unlimited amount of energy authentically available to you, so you can move through life in any direction you choose?... [Give time. Encourage]... Fabulous!

And if the mentor were to speak from the place of absolute freedom, what new support-ive, empowering and integrative truths or realizations would he/she suggest?... [Read old beliefs, then elicit new and empowering truths as antidotes. Give time. Let answer. Write down new truths]... Great!

So just allow the mentor to install these new, healthy truths into every cell of the body... [Read out new truths]... Just experience how it feels as the mentor infuses every fiber of your being with these brand new, wholesome realizations... drenching, filling, renewing all of consciousness with freedom and positivity .. making these positive and life affirm-ing capacities an organic and natural part of your being...

And when this is totally complete you can nod to let me know [Give sufficient time. En-courage]... Fabulous! Thank you.

Final Forgiveness

10. Now bring awareness back to the campfire, and those you were speaking with ear-lier, and ask the mentor what needs to happen here for complete forgiveness to flow in all directions? [Let that happen. If necessary, continue dialogue with the one person or both people previously addressed until partner is completely empty and forgiveness can flow naturally in all directions]

Go ahead and forgive all those at the campfire, sending them blessings. Allow them to merge into the fire, which is the infinite source of all life. Then turn to the **younger you** and **say:** "I promise you will never have to experience this again. I forgive you for any pain that was caused, and for not always having access to your deepest self, your true authenticity and expression at that time, but now you know that freedom is always here... always available because it is who you really are."

Then hugging the **younger you**, let yourself merge, allowing the **younger you** to grow up with this forgiveness and true authenticity already inside ... Turning to the **mentor**, thank him/her ... Now come back to the present and allow awareness to expand spa-ciously in front, vastly behind and openly to all sides, soaking as an ocean of presence.

Future Integration

11. Having learned what you've learned, having experienced what you've experienced - open into the consciousness of you a day from now, feel how you are feeling, breathe how you are breathing... How are you feeling?... Knowing that the authentic, free you is always your essence... imagine a situation arising that would have triggered the old patterns of closure or shut down. Notice how you are handling things now... How are you responding differently to life now?... How do you feel about yourself?

Now see yourself a week from now, open into the consciousness, feel how you are feeling, breathe how you are breathing... How are you feeling?... Imagine some old trigger or catalyst occurring... How differently do you respond now?... What kind of things are you saying to yourself?... How are you speaking and acting differently now?... And how are you feeling?

Step into the future a month from now and open into that consciousness... feel how you're feeling, breathe how you're breathing... How are you feeling?... What do you realize about the true nature of emotions... of life... of existence... of your real self?

Now open into the consciousness of you six months down the line. How are you feeling, about yourself, about freedom, about who you are and how you are living life? What is your deepest realization? What have you realized to be true about your essential self?

Now step into the future a year from now and ask: In this openness, this authenticity, this fullness of life ... this absolute freedom... What's the best that could happen?... And how does that feel?... [Let answer]... Thank you... And then what's the best that could happen? [Let answer]...Thank you... And how does that feel? [Repeat until partner feels positive and uplifted, and the question feels complete]

Let the free, wise fully authentic communicator that you are share some words of wisdom on how to be... how to live... giving practical advice on what to do to revel in this freedom... as an inspiring example of all the qualities of infinite awareness, of enlightened presence... [Give time. Let answer]

So, knowing that you will only be able to open your eyes as soon as all parts of you are completely integrated and agreed that the realization, freedom, clarity, and expansion that is here can only grow and deepen over time, and when all parts of you are agreed that this can take place perfectly, naturally of its own accord, effortlessly and gracefully, then you can softly open your eyes now, when you are ready.

Great work ... Congratulations!

As with the previous introspections, please now allow a little quiet time so the results of this process can begin to integrate. You may feel some temporary shakiness, wooziness or slight disorientation as your body adjusts to the emotional and physical shift that has just taken place - this is absolutely normal, and in fact is a positive signal that healing is happening. These effects will pass of their own accord, normally within an hour to a few hours, so there is nothing specific that you need to do. Just relax and let things resolve naturally, automatically. You can support yourself while this takes place by getting some rest and eating easily digestible food - something plain and simple and soothing - and maybe by taking a warm bath or shower. Then your body can focus on what it knows how to do: healing.

And when this re-adjustment is complete you will likely feel as if something deep has shifted, like a weight has been lifted or a tension released internally. These, again, are positive signs that transformation has taken place.

Give yourself some time, preferably at least 24 hours, before undergoing the next introspection. This is the last introspection included here and it is short and very easy. It is also deeply resolving and effective at helping us let go of unhealthy habits and patterns.

And before you move on, please recognize that at this point you have completed three major introspections: The Physical Journey, The Emotional Journey and The Worst-Best Journey. Take a moment to really congratulate yourself! You have done some amazing work, and it is time to take stock of some of the changes, the shifts that have taken place.

If you were to take just ten minutes and look back in your mind's eye to the time before you started doing the process work in this book, what has changed for the better? What has shifted emotionally? How has your life outlook altered in positive ways? How is your body responding more healthily?

Take this time to check yourself out, and write down some answers. It is always a good thing to do a comparison check after we have made some significant shifts - it helps keep us real, and helps keep us focused as we move forward. And there is only a short way to go now. We will finish our process work with something called a Six-Step Reframe - it is one of my favorite short interventions.

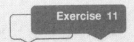
Exercise 11

Instructions: The Six-Step Reframe

Download the audio and script at www.kevinbillett.org/book-bonus

Intention:
That you communicate with your unconscious mind and get its cooperation to change a specific unhealthy pattern, habit or behavior
Time:
20 to 25 minutes
Emotional level:
Non-emotional
What you need:
Quiet space
At the end:
Break of 5 minutes or so

The following process is called a Six-Step reframe. It was originally developed in the field of Neuro-Linguistic Programming and is borrowed and adapted here for our specific purposes.

The Six-Step Reframe is based on the premise that there is a deep part of ourselves that automatically drives habitual behaviors or patterns, and that this part really intends us to benefit in some way (like keeping us safe or protecting us emotionally) when it does so - even when the behavior or pattern becomes unhealthy or detrimental. The process aims to empower that other-than-conscious part to make healthier choices and to find and automatically manifest more supportive patterns while maintaining the same benefits, or even creating better benefits for us. It is an elegantly effective intervention that is non-emotional.

Although it can be effective at any time, I would recommend that you undergo the previous Journeywork first and to do this process afterwards. Then you are more likely to get maximum benefit from the Six-Step Reframe. Please read at a normal conversational pace.

Beginning the Six-Step Reframe

Ask your partner to name the behavior or pattern associated with depression that they wish to change: this could be a specific behavior, habit or pattern, or it could be the whole pattern of depression itself. Then simply read this script out to you while they close their eyes, relax and allow the process to be effortless, easy and comforting. Your partner can rest in the knowledge know that a deep part of them, their other-than-conscious, will be doing all the work, so they can just sit and be still. They may not feel anything as the process progresses, or may simply find that they are quiet and meditative; either way is fine. **Your partner will not be required to speak, because you will be speaking to an other-than-conscious part in them, not directly to them.**

During the section where you ask the other-than-conscious part to give you a signal, if you do not see that signal just ask for it to be turned up, made more visible. If you still don't see the signal just thank the part and move on, it is not absolutely necessary to see it for the process to work perfectly.

Read the script at a moderate conversational pace, with very short pauses where you see "..." You can use a substitute name for the other-than-conscious part if your partner prefers.

Exercise 11: The Six-Step Reframe

> Note: Ask partner to name the pattern, habit of behavior they wish to change - this could be the pattern of depression itself or an associated habit. Read at a moderate conversational pace. Remember you are speaking to the 'part' responsible for generating the behavior or pattern and not directly to your partner.

*I'd like to speak to the part responsible for generating this _____ [Behavior, pattern, habit, etc.] And, as I don't know the name of this part, I'm going to call it the Guardian Part... unless there's another name you'd prefer... [Let give alternative if preferred]... because I know that there is a way in which this part has been protecting and taking care of _____ [Partner's first name] in the past... And the first thing I'd like to do is to thank the Guardian Part for **all** it has done to be a good guardian to _____ [Name] for a long time... maybe for many years... And I'd like to reassure this Guardian Part that **everything** I am about to say and do will be in full support of its job of making sure that _____ [Partner's name] gets the emotional benefits it is committed to getting... **everything** I do will only support the Guardian Part in providing these, and maybe even greater, benefits...*

And so, I'd like to ask the Guardian Part if it would be willing to signal me if I am in contact with it... and this signal could be a skin-color change, or a finger twitch, or a micro-muscle movement, or a noticeable change in breathing... in fact it can be any visible signal the Guardian Part feels appropriate... and _____ [Name] can just continue to relax more deeply while this happens... Good... And I'd be grateful if the Guardian Part could just intensify the signal a little... Great. Thank you.

> Note: It is helpful, but not necessary, that the signal is made. If you don't see it after asking that it be turned up, simply thank the part and move on regardless.

And now I'd like to ask the Guardian Part if it would be willing to communicate to _____ [Name's] conscious mind the emotional benefits that the behavior has been providing... and I'd like to reassure the Guardian Part that I will respect its desire for privacy if it feels that the conscious mind is not yet ready to receive that information... and if it is ready to communicate the benefits to the conscious mind, I'd like to ask the Guardian Part to give me a 'yes' signal, and to allow the communication to take place... Great...

*Now, I'd like to ask the Guardian Part to go to the **infinitely wise and all-creative part**... to the **higher self** or the **God-self** or **Source**, and ask that infinitely wise and all-creative self to generate **hundreds of healthy, alternative behaviors**... wonderful... and next,* *for the Guardian Part to choose from these **hundreds of alternative behaviors** at least **three alternative supportive behaviors** that are as immediate and effective at getting the same or even better benefits... choose at least **three alternative healthy behaviors** that will as immediately and effectively provide the same or better benefits... Good.*

And I'd like to ask the Guardian Part to give a clear signal when the choices have been made... Great!...

Now, I'd like to ask if there are any other parts that might object to these three alternative behaviors... and if there are any objections to signal clearly now... Great... Thank you...

> Note: It is helpful, but not necessary, that the signal is made. If do not see the signal just carry on normally with the process.

*So I'd like to ask the Guardian Part to join with these objecting parts and together to form a Team Guardian... and for this Team Guardian to go back to the **infinitely wise and all-creative part**... to the **higher self** or the **divine self** or **Source**, and to ask that infinitely wise and all-creative self to generate **hundreds more alternative healthy behaviors**... That's it... And for Team Guardian to select at least **three alternative supportive behaviors** that provide as immediate and effective benefits as the old behavior... perhaps far more and far better benefits... Great... And for Team Guardian to signal clearly when the choices have been made... Wonderful...*

*And, once again, I'd like to ask if there are any other parts that might object to these three alternative behaviors... and these may be shy or hidden parts... they may be parts stuck in dark places or in the corners... And so, I'd like to welcome forward **all** remaining objecting parts now... Great ... Thank you...*

*Now I'd like to ask all these remaining objecting parts to join with Team Guardian and form a Total Team Guardian... and for this Total Team Guardian to go back to the **infinitely wise and all-creative part**... to the **higher self** or **divine self** or **Source**, and to ask that infinitely wise and creative self to generate **hundreds more alternative healthy behaviors**... Great... That's it... And for Total Team Guardian to select at least **three alternative supportive behaviors** that provide as immediate and effective benefits as the old behavior... perhaps far more and far better benefits... Excellent! ... And for Total Team Guardian to signal clearly when the choices have been taken ... [Give a little time] ... Thank you ...*

> Note: Again, if you do not see the signal simply pause and then move on normally.

And now, I'd like to ask if all parts are in alignment and in agreement with the new behaviors... and if all parts are in alignment, to signal clearly by allowing _____ [Name] to take a nice deep breath in now ... [Give a little time. Take a deep breath in yourself] ... Thank you...

> Note: In the very rare case that your partner is unable to take a deep breath in, simply cycle again through Total Team Guardian paragraphs, welcoming all remaining objecting parts. Then move ahead normally.

*And so, now that all parts are in alignment, I'd like to ask Total Team Guardian if it would be willing to **take responsibility** for generating these **new, alternative healthy behaviors** for a period of just 10 days... and if it is willing, to signal 'yes' by allowing _____ [Name] to take another nice deep breath in now... [Give a little time. Take a deep breath in yourself]... Great.*

*Now I'd like to ask _____ [Name] to step into the future ten days from now, and to see and hear and feel what it is like now that you have been **free from the old behavior** for a period of ten days... and get a full sense of what you have been able to accomplish now that you are **generating new behaviors** that all parts are happy with... or perhaps you have been generating even better behaviors that have been revealed over the last ten days.*

*What does that really feel like... to be free from that old behavior... and generating these **brand new behaviors** that are so integrative and supportive?... Great... And now just imagine a situation arising that would previously have led to the old behavior, and see and hear and feel how **differently** you are responding and behaving, now that you are completely free... Wonderful...*

*And now step into the future six months from now, and let your body feel how good it is to have been **free from that old behavior** for a period of six months... What other healing has taken place during this time?... And in what unexpected ways has your life changed for the better now that you are **completely free from that ancient behavior**, and are generating much more resourceful behaviors that provide **at least** the same benefits?... Fabulous... And just bask in the consciousness of you six months from now, knowing that this wholeness, this consciousness is always present, always here... And now just come back to the present moment... And you may open your eyes now, when you are ready.*

Well done! Great work!

❖

Give yourself a little while to come around, relax and be still for a few minutes. There is nothing more to do here.

Then, over the coming days, you can just begin to notice the automatic shifts that are taking place in your behavior or pattern, as your other-than-conscious facilitates healthier choices and supports you in more wholesome and effective ways. Take note when you spot such changes in your day-to-day habits - you could even write them down in a notebook if you like - just to keep score of your wins.

Huge congratulations! You stuck it out. You did the work. You have completed all the closed eye introspections, all the deep emotional clearing work in this book! Great job!

I trust that by now you are experiencing significant shifts in your emotional wellbeing and in your attitude to life. If there are still some areas that need work it is simple - just go back to one of the three major processes here at any time and repeat it. It makes for good emotional housekeeping to clear out some old crud on a regular basis. Brandon and I do some version of these processes regularly, sometimes even once every week, because we know the body can hold onto a lot of past hurts and we want to stay as clear, open and vibrant in life as possible.

CHAPTER 10

Moving Forward Consciously

Positive Force #1: Supportive Lifestyle Choices

Now you have completed all the deep process work of the book you are ready to move forward into this next section. I hope that you are resting more naturally in yourself, feeling free, whole and at peace emotionally. You have completed the work, haven't you? If not, please consider going back to experience these liberating and transformative introspections. If you wish to be free from depression it is really important that you undergo this work before moving forward in the book.

In this chapter I'm going to cover some lifestyle choices you can make that will support you emotionally, physically and mentally in living healthily in your newfound freedom. Some areas will require you to recognize and be truthful about where problems exist. Some areas will require you to take action. So please read through this chapter once from beginning to end, and then come back and go through it again with a pen and notebook, so you can make some personal notes as your own circumstances come to mind and you make some decisions to change. You can then use your notes as a checklist to keep you on track.

First, full disclosure: I am not an expert in this area. The following should be treated as guidelines only, and I invite you to do your own research (there is plenty available online) and come to your own conclusions. The bottom line is that these are important areas to take into consideration when choosing a healthy and fulfilling way forward in life.

Planting SEEDS

One way to remember the five categories of lifestyle we need to address is to think about planting SEEDS: making changes to any unsupportive patterns in our sleep, exercise, environment, diet and sunshine intake.

Sleep

Current research has shown that we need quality sleep, about seven or eight hours of it per night, but many of us do not get it. Lack of sleep and disturbed sleep can directly influence our mood, so what can we do to improve our sleep time and quality?

• **Avoid eating food late at night.** Food - in particular heavy, rich, cooked food - takes a lot of energy to digest, and that digestion process can keep us awake. It is best to finish eating at least two or three hours before we go to bed, to give our bodies a chance to at least start the process and get some of the meal processed by the stomach and moving downwards.

• **Avoid excessive alcohol.** Small amounts of alcohol can relax us and make us sleepy, but larger amounts cause restlessness and poor quality sleep. Drink, if you choose to at all, only in moderation.

• **Avoid caffeine and caffeinated drinks**, including coffee, black tea and energy drinks, from lunchtime onwards.

• **Avoid dramatic, upsetting or violent programs before bedtime.** This includes playing computer games, watching television dramas, movies, and particularly news programs.

• **Avoid computers in bed.** The light they give off can signal our bodies to stay awake, not go to sleep. If you read in bed using an electronic book reader, choose one that has a dark screen with white writing option; the light is dimmer and is much more conducive to sleep. Or, use the lowest brightness setting available for the screen.

• **Keep your bedroom as dark as possible.** Even small amounts of light during the night can disturb us and keep us awake. Fit blackout drapes to keep outside light at bay, and take any non-vital electronic devices out of the bedroom; many of them have green, blue or red lights that never turn off and can disturb our sleep patterns.

• **Make sure the mattress on your bed is comfortable, and suits your size and weight.** Saggy, too-firm or too-soft mattresses keep us awake. Make sure your pillows and bed sheets are clean and comfortable; wash them with natural, irritant-free washing powders.

• **Let fresh air into your bedroom.** If it is safe to do so, keep a window cracked open to allow some fresh air into your bedroom. It helps.

• **Sleep cool.** When the bedroom temperature is too warm, it disrupts sleep. The best sleep temperature for most people is 64-70 degrees Fahrenheit. Much warmer than this and we tend to get overheated and restless.

• **If a sleep aid is needed, use melatonin.** Melatonin is a hormone that regulates our day-night cycles, our circadian rhythms, and as we get older its prevalence may subside in our bodies. You may wish to consider taking melatonin supplements on an as-needed or regular basis. Do some research on it and make your own mind up.

• **Get exercise.** Physical exercise helps us sleep... and is the topic of our next subject.

Exercise

The more I read about health, the more I read about the importance of regular physical exercise. It affects every part of our body-mind, and lack of it can be very detrimental to our wellbeing. Make a practice of regularly moving your body throughout the day. Start, if you need to, in simple ways, and as your strength improves you will find that your enthusiasm for it will increase.

• **Move.** Move in any way you can. Any movement is better than no movement. Even when you are sitting at home, stand up on a regular basis and just stretch your legs a little before sitting back down.

• **Walk.** Walking is great exercise, so make sure to fit in at least 45 minutes to an hour of it every day. It is surprising how quickly the time adds up if you change a few basic practices. If you drive, park your car a little further away than normal from your destination, and walk the rest of the way. If you are in a store or hotel, choose the staircase instead of the escalator or elevator. Use your own staircase at home as an exercise device. Some people choose to buy small pedometers that fit onto their belts, and aim to walk an average of 10,000 steps per day. In any case, just get walking.

• **Go to the gym.** Yeah, the gym - it works! Whether you choose aerobic training or resistance training, it is all beneficial, so renew your membership and work out. It will make you feel better. If you don't want to pay membership fees get some elasticated training bands; they are cheap, transportable and versatile, and they work too!

• **Swim.** Swimming is a fantastic form of exercise that works almost all of the body without stressing joints or weak areas. Get to the pool and start putting in some lengths, or get some lessons and learn how.

• **Yoga.** I can barely believe I am writing this here, because I really dislike yoga. But I must admit it is good for our flexibility, stamina and overall health. So sign up for a class, any type, it doesn't matter which, as long as you enjoy it and stick with it.

• **Play sports.** Anything you like, just play. Pretend to be a kid again and let loose a bit as you play - it's not about achieving anything or winning, it really is about taking part.

• **Make love.** It's a great way to get exercise and there is always the added benefit of the endorphins, the bliss chemicals it produces in our bodies!

• **Just move.** Make it social if that is your preference, make it private if that's your way, and whatever you do, move.

Environment

A healthy and supportive environment is deeply important to our emotional wellbeing. Dirt, clutter and disorder can be a reflection of our old mental and emotional states. Improving our living environment can be a powerful metaphor for improving our own sense of wellbeing and transforming our own lives.

• **Home environment.** Mess, clutter and dirt can creep up on us over time at home and can insidiously drag us down. Open your eyes and take a good hard look at what your home environment is like. Look at areas that have become grubby and clean them. Check your kitchen and throw out stale foods, cans that have passed their use by dates, anything that you bought and found you did not like, but are holding on to. Put it all in the trash. Check your bathroom cabinets and toss out toiletries you no longer use, leftover or half-squeezed toothpaste tubes whose flavor you disliked, makeup that didn't suit your skin tones. Again, throw it out.

Then check your closets and pull out the clothes that don't fit, the items you haven't worn in more than a year and give them to a thrift store, or sell them online. Be unsentimental and ruthlessly realistic; if you don't really like an item, if it is not really your color or your style, or if you simply do not think you will wear it in the next month, get rid of it. It is astonishing how much freshness, lightness and uplift can come from the simple act of letting go of what you don't want or need.

• **Work environment.** Check out your working environment and follow the same instructions as above. Clear out drawers, closets and desks. Sell, give away or throw away anything that is outmoded, unneeded or defunct. Take down old posters or artwork that no longer positively affect you. Throw away old diaries and schedules. Clear some space so you can breathe more easily, and be less distracted, more relaxed and creative at work.

• **Car.** Apply the same principles to your car as you would to your home or workplace. At a minimum, put it through the carwash and clean the inside, including the insides of the windows so you can see out more clearly. It is amazing what effect a dirty windscreen can have on our perception of life. Throw away any accumulated garbage, including in the trunk, and pump up the tires to their correct pressures. Check the oil, check the windshield washer water and, if the car needs it, get it serviced.

• **Relationships.** Relationships that are wholesome and supportive are one of life's most valuable and uplifting gifts. Relationships that are past their 'sell by' date are a drain on our emotional resources. Take an honest look at the relationships in your life. Do they all support and nourish you, or are there some that rob you of energy rather than giving you energy? Are there some you should give more time to and foster? Are there some you want to invest less time in? Are there others you should let go of altogether?

If you identify some that you should let go of then make that choice, let go and move on. If there is an emotional impact to the letting go, then go back to the Emotional Journey, the Physical Journey or the Worst-Best Journey introspections to help you deal with it, move through it and move on. If there are relationships (and I'm sure there will be some) that are not supportive but that cannot be changed, then you could choose to be honest and admit the emotional consequence of living with this relationship. Then, once again, you could use the three major introspections named above to face and burn through those emotional consequences.

Diet

Many of us have used food to alter our moods. We use sugars and chocolate, for instance, to give us a lift; we eat heavy starchy foods or drink alcohol, for instance, to cover or suppress emotions that we don't want to feel. Comfort eating of any type gives us the possibility of a short-term shift in our feelings, but normally comes with a heavy medium to long term price - in terms of weight gain, tiredness and many other health issues that can feed into the loop of depression.

If we have faced and cleared some of our hooks relating to the drivers of our depression patterns, we can often find that our bodies will automatically respond by dropping the need for unhealthy foods and naturally wanting to eat more healthily and supportively. Of course, it helps to be clear about what is healthy and what is unhealthy. Here are some very basic guidelines.

• **Avoid sugars.** Sugars, particularly refined sugars, are poisons. Unfortunately they are hidden in almost every type of packet or processed food, including most packaged cereals, pre-cooked meals, fast foods and sodas. Much modern research is proving that refined sugars are about the worst types of food we can ingest. They hijack the same neural pathways as drugs like cocaine, and they are addictive. They are the major cause of the world's current explosion in incidence of diabetes and metabolic syndrome, and some research has linked sugar consumption to mood swings and depression. Check all packaged foods for sugar content, and I think you will be shocked. Limit your total daily sugar intake to no more than 15 grams.

• **Limit processed carbohydrates.** Processed carbohydrates such as breads, cookies and pasta possess few or no real nutrients, and quickly turn to sugars inside the body.

• **Avoid trans fats.** Trans fats mess with your cholesterol levels and cause arterial hardening and arteriosclerosis. They are common in French fries, fried chicken and fish, microwave popcorn and many pastries. Cut them out altogether if possible.

• **Limit caffeine.** Overexposure to caffeine, mainly from drinking coffee, sodas or caffeine-laden 'energy' drinks, can cause dehydration, anxiety, insomnia and a host of other physical symptoms. Keep it in check.

• **Avoid GMO foods.** There are many arguments for and against genetically modified foods. The bottom line is that GMO crops either rely on an increased amount of harmful pesticide in order to grow, or they are designed to themselves produce chemicals that act as insecticides. Do your own research and decide… but in my opinion they are potentially harmful to our health.

• **Increase consumption of fresh, organic vegetables.** Most fresh vegetables are not dense in calories yet, as well as being generally nourishing, they contain minerals, vitamins, phytochemicals, enzymes and antioxidants that are all helpful in sustaining good health.

• **Increase consumption of fresh organic fruits.** Fruits are similar to vegetables in the benefits they can bring to health, but watch out for hidden sugars. The fructose (sugar) in fruit metabolizes more healthily than does refined sugar, but still be aware that some fruits have high sugar contents.

• **Eat nuts, seeds and pulses.** Raw nuts, seeds and pulses contain healthy fats, vitamins and antioxidants. Nuts and seeds can be calorie dense, so eat relatively small portions regularly. Cooked pulses can generally be eaten more freely.

• **Increase healthy oils.** Many people recommend olive oil, citing studies around the Mediterranean style diet. Recently coconut oil has been attracting a lot of positive press for its health giving qualities, and is also recommended for cooking and frying. Be aware, though, that Omega-6 oils and vegetable oils such as sunflower oil and canola are not in the same category and are not thought to be healthy.

• **Increase clean water intake.** It is vital for your digestion, healthy organ function and your overall health that you drink sufficient clean, preferably filtered, water. Aim for around six to eight medium sized glasses every day.

Sunshine

In recent decades there has been a strong movement warning us of the dangers of sunshine. It causes skin cancer, the messages tell us, so we should cover up, slather sunscreen on our skin or avoid going outdoors when it is sunny. And while there is direct evidence that links overexposure to sunshine and burning to skin cancers, there is another important side to this story.

Sunshine creates vitamin D, and it affects every organ of the body. Vitamin D, in truth more a hormone than a vitamin, is vital for the health of virtually every part of our body; there is even some recent research that indicates that it directly affects the expression of some 3,000 genes in our DNA. There is more research that shows that a lack of vitamin D can directly contribute to a wide variety of cancers. We need it to survive, yet most of the western world is now experiencing a massive and dangerous drop in vitamin D levels. And low vitamin D levels can have a huge impact on our happiness as well as our health.

Current recommendations (ones that seem sensible to me) say that we should, as far as is possible, get 15 to 20 minutes of sunshine on our bare skin each day, so that we can boost our Vitamin D back to normal levels. Get your vitamin D levels checked; there is a good chance they are low. And get out in the sunshine, avoiding those synthetic sunscreens that have known carcinogenic ingredients. Please be sensible, and do not allow your skin to burn while you get some sunshine.

- **Get outdoors**, with at least 40 per cent of your skin exposed to direct sunshine - shorts and a short-sleeved shirt would achieve that. Your facial skin is thinner than the skin on most other parts of your body and needs more protection, so wear a hat that give you sufficient shade or apply some natural, organic sunscreen. Be sensible and do not allow your skin to burn.

- If you live in a part of the world, as I do, where sunshine is a rare or distinctly seasonal commodity, **take oral vitamin D3 supplements combined with vitamin K2 and magnesium.** Do some research on current recommended dosages - they may be higher than you expect, at around 5,000iu to 10,000iu per day for adults.

Finally,

- **Do things that are fun!** Do anything that gives you joy - dance, sing, play, write, play a musical instrument, experiment with cooking, get creative with some gardening, tell jokes, be silly, tell people you love them - do anything that gets your juices flowing, your adrenaline flowing, and allows you to connect more fully with yourself, with loved ones, with nature.

Making Healthier Choices

Remember to go back through this chapter and make some personal notes, make some decisions and write down your fresh intentions. Staying healthy and staying positive and depression free are often intertwined functions, so choose to improve your health and energy levels.

If you find yourself unmotivated at any point, or if you slip back into old ways, just stop, open and feel what you are feeling emotionally. Then refer back to the guided introspections, and go again through one of the main clearing processes - either the Worst/Best or the Emotional Journey. This will help you to get to the emotions and clear the hooks around any associated issue. Then you'll find that your natural motivation, energy and the willpower to move forward healthily and self-supportively in life will increase in leaps and bounds.

Once you have made the lifestyle and health decisions you need to make and have put a plan into action, then and only then, will you be ready to move forward to the next chapter. There we will explore some approaches we can take to developing purposeful and purpose-led lives that are rich with meaning and fulfillment.

CHAPTER 11

Moving Forward Consciously

Positive Force #2: Discovering Your Life's Purpose

When I was growing up the subject of purpose in life never arose, it was never discussed in my family. The idea that life could be lived purposefully was a notion that we never contemplated. Our view of life was, I suppose, a simplistic one. It seemed reasonable and pragmatic to know that you did not complain at what life had given or not given you; you just got on with the job of living, worked hard at whatever you chose or were destined to do, did a good job, made money, saved, climbed the success ladder so you would eventually acquire the means to fund the lifestyle that would make you happy and fulfilled.

You already know from previous chapters how unsuccessful, and ultimately disillusioning, that philosophy proved for me. But as well as not working as a happiness plan, the 'do whatever you need to do to make enough money to be happy' strategy produced a subtly undermining side effect: it fed the subterranean feelings of pointlessness that I already experienced in life, and over time caused them to grow into a recognizable and often felt sense of purposelessness.

Even (maybe especially) during the times in my adult life that I was most financially successful, I felt as if what I did as a career - wholesaling and retailing jewelry - had no real value in it and was essentially devoid of purpose.

From time to time it was pleasant to help couples find the perfect engagement ring or wedding ring, or to assist someone in choosing a gift that would be cherished; I could share to some extent in the joy of that. But the pervasive sense I had was that I had chosen a career where the primary, most important, goal was to make money. And my job often felt meaningless and empty.

I sometimes contemplated what I could do career-wise that would have some real value, and concluded that it would have to be something that made a positive difference in the lives of other people - but I did nothing about it. And then, as you know, my life imploded until I underwent my first Journey process and profoundly healed almost every aspect of my life.

When I walked out of that first session with Bill I had no job, almost no money, and no home of my own; I had separated from Karen and moved in to live with my father. Within a week I received a phone call from Ron and Bob, two friends who were also colleagues. They invited me to work fulltime in a consultancy partnership that I had previously worked in on an ad hoc basis. It seemed like a financial lifeline.

I knew that I badly needed the income, that I had spousal support and child maintenance payments to consider, and that I would shortly need to find a place of my own and pay rent and normal living expenses. But there was a part of me that balked at committing fulltime to the consultancy. I was feeling clear and healthy in my being, but my belly felt a crimping sensation, a distinct glitch at the prospect of fulltime work. It was a feeling that I was not used to, but I listened to it.

There was a part of me that wanted more flexibility, a part that did not want to be so tied down with regular hours. I had no specific plans about what I wanted to do with my spare time, but my intuition was to create some free time in my life.

So I phoned Ron and Bob and, without fully understanding why I was doing it, negotiated with them: if they would agree to a guaranteed income plus a share of profits, I would work at least three days a week on the venture. They agreed. I sacked my psychiatrist, weaned myself of the medications I had been taking, and went to work part-time.

Within a very short time it became clear why I had resisted a fulltime commitment. Brandon's new work, called The Journey, had already received an enthusiastic response in the UK and she decided to offer weekend workshops. I knew that she already had a promoter, so that end of things was handled, but I felt a strong urge to contribute, to help. Since I had benefitted so massively from Journeywork, I felt a deep passion to get the word out so others could benefit too.

When next we spoke I made her an offer that required no thought, no consideration: "I will do anything I can to help you get this work out there, Brandon. Just tell me what you want and I will do my best to do it. I only work three days a week so I have plenty of spare time. I have a background in business, so I could help organizationally; I have a car and can drive you to your appointments or just generally fetch and carry. I will organize and run the sound from the back of the room at your upcoming events; I will be a trainer and support the participants at the events; I will do anything you ask to the best of my abilities. I don't need to be paid for it... just, please, don't ask me to stand up in front of people and speak!"

The words came out of my mouth before I realized what I was offering, but the offer and the commitment felt more right than any other work commitment I had ever made. My gratitude for what I had received needed to be reciprocated, not necessarily by offering something back personally to Brandon, but more by offering something of potential value to other people who needed help, who had life issues like I had had, and who did not yet know about this new work.

Brandon accepted my offer and I threw myself into the new and unfamiliar arena of seminar organization. I loved every moment of it, was in awe of the work and the radical, profound healing effects I began to see it having on many people's lives. For the first time ever I knew that my life had meaning, had true purpose. I was reminded of that truth every time I looked into the eyes of someone who had experienced a breakthrough such as my own. I felt it every time someone reported that they had resolved an emotional or a health issue that they never thought it possible to heal from. And I absolutely knew it every time I underwent another Journey process and cleared more layers of pain and hurt from my own life.

For the first time in my life I had found work that I felt had real value. It seemed compellingly natural that I wanted to share it with others: not by preaching or proselytizing about what it could do, but by walking my talk, by clearing any remaining issues that I became aware of in my own life, by being an example of the possibility of human transformation, and by quietly offering that same possibility to anyone who had the courage to stop, open and feel.

I wanted not to speak about the possibilities, but to embody them, to be them. I had a fierce desire to push the boundaries deep and wide in my own life, to find out how much transformation was possible, how much freedom was available. And I wanted whatever changes occurred in me to stand as an inspiration, an invitation, to others.

As my own introspections and clearing processes did their work, I began to feel more at home in my own skin, and at the same time felt both lighter in my being and even more grounded in inner stillness. I felt more fulfilled than I had ever imagined possible, and I fell more and more deeply in love with Journey-work and its profound benefits.

Over the ensuing year or so, Brandon and I enjoyed a sweet and tender friend-ship, focused mostly on reaching out to people with The Journey, but including also a personal and mutually supportive quality. I felt a soft protectiveness to-wards her, and intense gratitude for developing the work that had lifted me out of depression.

Then something shifted, deepened between us.

We were both single and available, and one day decided to get clear on what we ideally wished for in a life partner. We individually sat, got still and began to create our 'values list', the list of the qualities we most prized and wanted in a future significant other. My list included self-realization, integrity, openness, honesty, emotional availability, attractiveness, sensuality, intelligence, positivity, adventurous and so on. We each wrote down twenty-something qualities that were important and desirable for us, and then we compared notes.

That our lists were very similar was the first surprise to us, but our surprise quickly turned into the warm sinking realization that we each exuded the quali-ties we looked for in an ideal mate. It seemed like a divine sign.

Of all the qualities I wrote down, Brandon exemplified every single one. Of all the qualities she wrote down, I apparently exemplified all but the last one. She had written 'Financially independent', and I was broke.

We checked our lists a second time, just to make sure we weren't missing anything. My heart began to flutter, my body subtly shook and my face began to flush with embarrassment. I sensed some difference in Brandon, too. She too seemed a little flushed, more or differently open towards me.

"I suppose you could work on the financial independence," she said softly, smiling.

And so began a soft courtship, and at first a rather tentative falling in love. We lived on different continents - she in the USA and I in the UK - so our relationship was mostly long-distance, although she more frequently spent time in London, and I occasionally visited her home in California.

We continued to work together as much as we could to jointly explore the possibilities Journeywork had to offer the world.

Then, at dinner together one evening, I spoke something that had been arising strongly inside me. "I want to be your manager," I said. "The Journey is the most extraordinary method of personal transformation that I could ever imagine, and I want to work full time with you, helping promote the work and getting it known worldwide. I want to travel with you, and be involved in this fulltime. It will take about 12 to 18 months for me to wind down my involvement with my consultancy, so I think there should be a transition period to allow us to figure out how it can work. I think I'm asking for a job!"

"Oh," Brandon replied, "That's a bit sudden. Let me consider it overnight. I'll come back to you about it tomorrow."

She came back to me at lunch the following day. "I've been opening with your request," she said, "and I accept. I have only one condition: you need to start tomorrow!"

I felt a heady mixture of fear and excitement. I was worried about the requirement of finding a way out of my business partnership with no notice, but I was elated at the possibility of completely offering myself to the work I loved so much. And so, I joined Brandon full time, as lover and as business partner, and we set about creating a life together as we founded the companies that would form the base of The Journey organization.

Through all the ensuing years I have fallen more deeply in love with the extraordinary, rare and wonderful woman, Brandon, who married me on the island of Maui in 1998.

And ever since those heady, life changing days I have felt the hand of grace in my life, guiding me, steering me, pulling me forward. Sometimes it has felt scary, as if life is asking too much from me, stretching me too quickly out of my comfort zones into unfamiliar territories. Sometimes it has been a wild adventure ride, exhilarating and uplifting. And for every single day of the last 24 years, the work Brandon and I do together with our extraordinary team of co-workers - who seem far more like family than like colleagues - is more deeply and richly rewarding and fulfilling than I could have possibly imagined work to be. Every day feels as if it is deeply and profoundly on purpose.

Opening to the Purpose of Your Life

I am repeating myself here because this is vitally important: you need to have finished all of the clearing processes in Chapter 9, and have made and put into action your lifestyle changes plan from Chapter 10 before undergoing the upcoming introspection. Please make sure you have done so before moving on to the next section.

The last step is to explore what it would take for you to live a life of meaning, of real value, of purpose. We will approach the question in a simple and practical way, so let's explore.

Instructions: Discovering What Gives You Purpose

Download the audio and script at www.kevinbillett.org/book-bonus

Find a comfortable chair, sit down and take a few moments to unwind... Now take a good, long, deep breath in... and slowly let it all the way out... right to the end of the breath... And another fresh, long, deep breath in... and as you breathe out now, let go of all tensions, all holding... just blow them out... and allow yourself to deeply relax...

Intention:
That you discover what gives, or could give you, a sense of meaning and purpose in life

Time:
45 to 50 minutes

Emotional level:
Mildly to moderately emotional

What you need:
Quiet space. Pen and paper. Tissues

At the end:
Break of 15 minutes or so

Exercise 12: Discovering what gives you purpose

Keep breathing this way... deeply, slowly in... fully, even more slowly out... Let each breath draw you inwards, and cause you to relax, as you become present to the pure presence, the awareness that is always here...vast and spacious...

Now, allowing your eyes to close, and to open or close again as and when necessary... begin inquiring: What are you most grateful for in life? Start with the small things, even if they seem insignificant... without censorship let the words find their way onto a new page in your notebook... What are you most grateful for? If you were grateful for some things in life, what would they be?

Can you dress yourself, for instance? Can you feed yourself, walk, see, hear, feel? There are many people who cannot... Do you have shelter to keep you warm, enough food to

keep you healthy? There are many people who do not... Do you have the friendship or love of people you care about?... Just begin writing without thinking; let it all arise from the heart of spacious awareness... of its own accord.

How have you been blessed in life? In what ways are you privileged? Write it down.

What things, what material gifts has life showered you with?... Where have you been, what have you experienced that you are grateful for?... Who are you grateful for in any area of your life?... Write all these things down... and keep writing until you feel that there is a natural pause or end to the outpouring... Take at least 10 minutes to complete this part of the exercise.

And now take a further 2 or 3 minutes to look back through what you have written, all the things you are grateful for, and pick at least five that are your favorites... and put a star next to each of them... You may find that some other inspiration arises as you are doing this. If it does, make a note of some other things that you are grateful for... and drink in the experience of gratitude... let it fully saturate your being.

And now, for a moment, having embraced this sense of gratitude, close your eyes... and inquire in a different way: What are some of the highlights of your life? What are some of the top experiences you have been through? What are the times when you felt the best, the most excited, elated, uplifted, loved, loving, satisfied, fulfilled, on purpose in life?... Let the answers bubble up automatically from the depth of your being, from the place that is much deeper than your thinking mind... What are your life's highlights, its pinnacles of experience?...

Take a few moments, and then, as before, just allow the words to pour onto a fresh notebook page... No thinking or screening of the words, just automatic writing... Let all your heightened experiences, the very best ones, find their way onto the page... You can if you wish close your eyes to access the memories, and then open them to do the writing... Name the specific experiences, and write down just enough words that you evoke the feelings you felt at that time... Take at least 10 minutes to do this... Go until it feels like there is a natural pause...

Good... Now, in the same way begin to inquire: When have you felt best about yourself in life?... When did you feel the most gratified, the most fulfilled, the most complete and happy?... When in life have you felt that you were really on track, truly on purpose?... When have you felt that life itself was using you in the perfect way, calling on your greatness, pulling forth your inspiration and guiding you?... When did you feel the simple, pure 'rightness' of the actions you were automatically taking?... Write all this down... Again, take about 10 minutes and write down just enough about each specific experience that it evokes the positive feelings you felt at that time... Write until there is a natural pause...

Great... And now, once again, take a look back through these last two sections, at the experiences that have been most meaningful in your life... And drink them in... adding stars alongside the most important ones, the best of them...

Now, take a look back through all the starred items on your list... and one by one, start-ing with the gratitude section and working forward, open with each point... and drink it in... Go to each star and open with that event, or thing, or person... and get a sense of how that makes you feel emotionally... Ask how this really makes you feel... What emotions arise?...

Next to each star write down a short list of the emotions that arise when you contem-plate this facet of your life... Take around 5 minutes to do this... and with each emotion you write down, open your body to experience it physically, viscerally.

Excellent!... And now, feeling these positive emotions and allowing them to wash through your body... basking in their richness... and remembering that when life show-ers you with blessings it is a signpost, a notice that you are on track... in the right place, at the right time...

And now inquiring: if life, grace, the universe, were to guide you, or pull you forward from here onwards... what might it ask of you?... If it were not up to you... if it were up to life itself to make things clear... to make the decision for you... in which direction would it pull you?... What would it want you to do?.. How would it want you to contribute?... What would feel purposeful and right?... What would be most fulfilling?...

Knowing that you are an integral part of life, an essential and priceless part of the whole... and knowing that as life supports itself it is simultaneously supporting you... as part of that whole... what does life want from you?... How does it wish you to serve, to give back, to offer thanks and value?...

Close your eyes for a few minutes and allow whatever impulse wishes to arise from the depth of you begin to arise and be felt... Place all awareness inside your body... Let your mind soften and being to fall away... Let the revelation come from deep in your heart, your belly... even deeper, from your essence... What does life wish that will grace you in the giving of it?... What service, however small, would life love to see from you?...

When you are ready, you can open your eyes and write down whatever arises... Let the writing be free form, automatic... Let it be none of your business what is written... You can just witness it as the words form on the page...

Keep writing until you feel empty. Let it effortlessly flow out of you... Let the words pour, even if they make no sense in the moment of writing, until they naturally stop...

Excellent!... And now, take a look back through this last section... open with each sentence and feel its emotional impact... How would it make you feel if you were to let go, to surrender, to let life pull these actions, this service out of you?... How would it all really feel?... Write down the emotions that arise for you.

And finally, close your eyes for one last time, asking: if you were to make a commitment to taking some small actions, within the next 24 hours, to concretize this new way of moving forward... to let the universe know that you are willing, and are playing your part in whatever mystery is about to unfold... what commitments are you willing to make? What will you do?

Write down the commitments you are willing to make to yourself, to life...

When you are done, take a fresh, long, deep breath in... and let it all the way out...

Well done!

Your body and being should feel imbued and inspired by this purpose. From here forward life can be an ongoing lesson in listening to you heart and your body, and being guided by them.

Conclusion: Living in Freedom

If you have really opened emotionally in the reading of this book I trust that you have gained a large number of insights, into the condition of depression and into the condition of being human. I hope these insights have helped bring some clarity into areas of your life where there was previously confusion or misunderstanding.

And if you fully engaged with all the process work outlined here, I am sure that you have made some significant internal shifts. You now realize life holds more options and more freedom than you were previously aware of, you feel more healthy and whole as a being, your general emotional state has improved and you are aware of healthier options that you can take as you move forward in life.

There are a few extra techniques and understandings that will be useful to you as you move on.

The Essence of this Work

The essence of the work contained in this book is very simple; it can lead to deep healing and profound self-realization, and the invitation is not complex. Although some of our techniques and recommendations may at first seem a little unusual, they can be summarized very easily like this:

- **Stop** - occasionally at least. Stop all distractions. Stop all activity. Stop the habitual stories you have been telling yourself. Be still for a while in this present moment with nothing to do, no role to play, nothing to achieve. Stay awake to life with all its circumstances and just be with it.

- **Open**. Sit down and close your eyes. Relax from head to toe. Let your mind, your body, your whole being soften and open.

• **Feel**. Welcome your emotions to arise, be fully felt and naturally ebb away in their own time. This is not an invitation for catharsis, or acting out of emotions. It is a simple request to occasionally at least welcome them in silence, embrace them and let them be really, truly felt.

• **Dive In**. If you are willing to dive completely into the core of any emotion, no matter how strong it is or 'negative' you perceive it to be, it will reveal itself as an opening into pure energy, life force, freedom, the infinite, Source itself. Opening into Source in this way means you can access the extraordinary guidance that is born from the innate genius and wisdom of your soul. Every answer you ever sought is available to you. Everything you ever reached for, dreamed of, longed to access or feel is revealed to be already present, inside you, as you!

• **Empty Out**. Be willing to speak out loud, so your own ears can hear, the words related to old hurts that you have hung on to. Allow yourself to empty out from your body's cells all the old pains and hurts that may have been stuck there for years. The best place to do this is probably at the campfire in a Journey process, where a full healing conversation can take place, and you could also just find a quiet place and speak it out to the wall.

• **Forgive**. Forgiveness is the most potent healing communication that we can give to ourselves and to others. When we forgive we do not necessarily condone or approve of other people's past actions, we do not open ourselves to abuse. When we genuinely forgive, we let go, we open to deep peace and resolution in our being. As Nelson Mandela said, "Holding on to resentment is like drinking poison and expecting your enemy to die." Choose forgiveness as a way of life so your own resentments can heal and leave, and your whole being can come to peace.

• **Be Truthful**. Once you have experienced the truth of your own innate beauty, your own inner greatness, be honest about it. Open with it and share it with others, from a place of innocence and gratitude. Who you really are needs nothing added to it, does not need to be seen in a special light, does not need flattery or approval - it just IS. You are not separate from life; you are always included as an integral part of the totality of life.

The Opposite of Depression

In my seminars, the question sometimes arises, 'What is the opposite of depression?' Attendees often respond, 'Joy', 'Happiness', 'Positivity' and so on, naming emotions that they prize or reach for in life.

My answer to this question is different. When we recognize that depression is really a pattern of emotional shutdown that becomes habitual, we can easily appreciate that the opposite of depression is the ability and habit of feeling any clear, clean emotion! Any emotion you can name, if felt in openness, allowed to come and allowed to go with no story added, is the opposite of depression. Even the emotions you might in the past have avoided or feared can be the opposite of depression. Anger, rage, devastation, fear itself, when dived into and fully met are all the opposite of shutdown; they can be and are the opposite of depression.

So, if you ever again ask yourself, 'How will I know if I am depressed or not depressed?' one easy way to check is simply to enquire, 'What am I really feeling emotionally in this moment?' If you are able to name a specific emotion, and if you are then willing to welcome it - whatever it is - and feel it fully, then you are no longer perpetuating the pattern of depression. You have cracked it, and you are healthy, free.

Inner Listening

The best technique for making healthy decisions in life is to listen carefully to your body, and not to your thoughts. Our mind can be very sneaky, contriving to convince us that it knows best, that it always makes healthy choices for us when, in fact, it is simply manipulating in an attempt to keep some feared emotions under wraps. The body is a far more reliable and supportive decision making tool.

The Max Planck Institute reported several years ago that it had located the same neurons that exist in the brain throughout the human digestive tract. They called it the 'second brain'. Your gut instincts are often sound, and there is a good technique you can use to access the body's superlative inner knowing quickly. It is a technique we both use.

If you are faced with, let's say, an either/or choice, you simply stop, open and relax, inviting the thinking mind to soften and gently come to rest. Then, with eyes closed, you sense internally, into the spacious awareness that is always present inside. Next, into that neutral, open space you welcome the first choice - you might repeat the words associated with it or you could allow the awareness of it to arise - and you notice how the body automatically viscerally responds to that choice. Does your body glitch or crimp? Does it brace or somehow contract physically? Pay close attention to the sensation that arises. Next, you come back to neutral open awareness and then welcome the second choice to be felt by your body in the same way. Again, you notice how the body, not your thinking mind, automatically responds to this choice.

Then you simply compare your physical responses to the relevant choices. If your body stays open and relaxed, if it remains expansive, or if it feels internally like fresh air, all easy-breezy then the body is signaling that it is safe or healthy or beneficial to take this choice, and to move forward with confidence.

If, however, your body contracts or glitches, or if there is some sense of physical closure or retreat, or if your body senses some revulsion or pain then beware. In this case your body is signaling either a 'no' or a 'not now' to this choice, and it is asking you, at least for the moment, to make a different choice or to do nothing.

For many years Brandon and I have let our bodies' wisdom make our life choices, and we often stop to appraise in exactly this way. When we follow our bodies' advice it seems as if life's doors open before us, and progress is easy, effortless and constructive. If, however, we ignore our inner guidance, overriding it with some notion or egotistical idea of what 'we need' or what 'should happen', then we can normally look out! For then we can be sure that, at least for a while, we are going to be picking up some pieces, and we know exactly what we did to co-create whatever drama or unsupportive result has manifested.

So, if you want wise advice, **listen to your body**.

Come to Peace with Life's Circumstances

We have seen earlier in the book that adverse circumstances alone do not create depression. It is how we respond to difficult situations, internally by interpreting them and adding particular meaning to them and externally by how we react or act, that shapes our emotional response to our environment and life events.

I have witnessed many times over the years people afflicted by very serious, even life threatening, challenges who have responded by stopping long enough to get real with their situation, and then finding the courage to turn and truly face the pain of their circumstance. These were people who put out strong prayers to be free and healthy, then surrendered: they surrendered to the deepest emotions their situations triggered in them, and they surrendered into the core of those often devastating or overwhelming emotions; then they surrendered to the will of life, to grace itself - they handed over control to a power greater than themselves, and they trusted. These were extraordinary souls who found peace in the heart of the most racking of life events.

When we are faced with serious challenges in life we can do two things. We can open with the emotional consequences of that situation and surrender to it. We can let go and trust that the highest and best will happen, and we can cooperate with life by taking whatever actions are necessary to resolve or heal that circumstance. We have often seen what might be described as 'miracles' of healing, of transformation and of resolution take place when we face up to reality, let go of the notions of resistance and control, and then take conscious actions. It takes my breath away to witness others' courage and it awes me to see what life, given full rein, is capable of manifesting.

The second choice we can make is to recognize that some circumstances are not resolvable. There are some deals that cannot be changed, some factors that are apparently truly outside of our control or our influence. Then we can actively choose to surrender to the emotional consequence of completely accepting things as they are - with eyes wide open, we simply stop fighting life.

As our wonderful friends Miten and Deva Premal sing in their song Ananda, 'If you don't fight with life, life simply helps you... lifts you on its shoulders...'

And as our dear friend and spiritual beloved Gangaji once wrote, 'Truly, what's meant to be is. The peace is always in that.' In other words it is only our fighting with what is that makes it wrong and causes us pain. When we choose to embrace reality as it is, the opportunity for peace is always present.

Our spiritual teacher, HWL Poonja (Papaji) said, 'That which comes and that which goes is not real. Stay focused on what does not come and does not go, for that is your true self.' Emotions come and emotions go: let them, for they are not real. Circumstances come and circumstances go: let them, for they too are not real. Depression comes and depression goes: let it, for it was never really yours, it was never the ultimate truth. Keep your attention on that which is much deeper, far more profound; pay full attention to that which neither comes nor goes - the deepest truth of your essential being.

Practice Gratitude

Brandon always says, "Gratitude draws grace." And I think she is right. The practice of gratitude is supportive at more than one level.

In the simplest of terms the expression of gratitude refocuses and recalibrates our current experience and appreciation of life. In a purely practical way, getting clear about and writing down the things, people and experiences that we are most grateful for in life draws our attention in an organic way to the positives, the benefits and blessings we are graced by.

It is all too easy to let our tensions and complaints become the main focus of our attention and, what you focus on becomes more dominant, more prevalent. So choosing to be deeply honest about even the simple things, the things you may perhaps take for granted in life, can directly impact your sense of wellbeing and positivity.

Take, for example, things as basic as feeding yourself, dressing yourself, walking, moving, having shelter, keeping warm, having friends, family... Many people cannot do these things, do not have these advantages in life. So take stock.

At a deeper level gratitude seems to be a magnet for more of what we really want in life. It is an esoteric proposition that Brandon encapsulated elegantly in her wonderful book Freedom Is when she wrote a short story. In it she asked, if you had two neighbors, one of whom was a complainer, a whiner, a 'cup-always-half-empty' type of person, and the other who was grateful, appreciative and a 'cup-always-half-full' sort, in their time of need who would you be most prone to reach out to and help? The one who was already grateful and appreciative, right? Well, it works similarly at an unseen level in life: gratitude for what already is in our lives seems to magnetize more of what our hearts and souls truly desire.

So, my suggestion is that you do something very simple. Each night before bed, or each morning when you awaken, just write down in a journal three to five things that you are most grateful for in life. Start with the simplest blessings and let them progress. Write something different each day, it will take you just a few minutes. You'll be surprised how much you have to be grateful for, and you may be surprised how your changing focus helps you manifest more of what you really want in life.

Remember Where True Fulfillment Comes From

We have a saying that's often repeated in The Journey: 'Nothing on the outside can give you anything lasting.' It's a profound truth.

So often, as I did in the past, we make the mistake of believing that the cause of our dissatisfaction or unhappiness in life is something that's missing. We believe that we need something that we don't already have, something extra in order to be complete, feel good about ourselves, be happy.

So we chase 'the dream'. We strive and seek to fill the hole of 'lack' that we perceive is inside us. We work and strategize and contrive to acquire more; more of all the stuff that we feel will give us 'it' - whatever is lacking. We buy clothes and makeup and gadgets and cars and houses, in the hope that these things will bring lasting fulfillment. We fall into relationships, expecting our partners to make us feel loved, whole, desirable, and we seek fulfillment in romance or sex or some family ideal. We strive to pass an exam and gain some certificate of recognition or earn a job promotion and a bigger salary.

And although any of these accomplishments, acquisitions or activities may give us a temporary lift, a buzz or high, the feeling never lasts. The bliss of a new relationship, the rush of buying a new car, the excitement of an exotic vacation or the high of a financial windfall; none of it is permanent, none of it produces any fundamental shift in the way we perceive and feel about ourselves and our lives.

Even though Brandon and I have lived in a deeply loving, mutually supportive and often bliss-filled relationship for more than 20 years, we still know that ultimately neither of us completes or fulfills anything in the other. At the deepest level we cannot give each other anything. What we can do is bring innate love, wholeness and wellbeing to the relationship, and we can dance lightly and delightfully in that.

The only way to find true fulfillment is to stop and turn to face anything that appears to stand between you and that fulfillment - for example, in the way we have been exploring and putting into practice in this book. For when you are willing to embrace, accept and surrender to what you have previously resisted or suppressed, your own true nature becomes more and more obvious. It simply reveals itself, becomes self-evident. And that true nature is and always has been full, complete, whole, at peace - perfect just the way it is.

The words of the wonderful Indian sage, Ramana Maharshi, speak profoundly to this realization, "Bliss is not added to your nature. It is merely revealed as your true natural state, eternal and imperishable."

What to Do When Someone Close to You Has Depression

Get them to talk. Any type of positive communication can be good, and opening into a rapport and sharing emotionally is a big step. It shocks me that to this day there are still taboos around discussing depression, like there is something shameful about admitting that you might be depressed, or even in simply mentioning the word. So bring it out into the open; it's the only way you can begin to debunk these stupidly restricting notions, and give yourself the chance of doing some good.

Let your friend or loved one know that they are far from alone in experiencing what they are going through. Many people in the world experience some form of depression at some point in life. Speak from compassion, and gently tell them that help is available, and that many people have used various therapies and techniques - including the Journeywork in this book - to free themselves completely from depression, even when they did not believe it possible.

If they are open to it, suggest that they read this book. It would help if you have read it first and undergone the work here, so you can speak about it from firsthand experience.

Avoid offering platitudes. Though often well meant, phrases such as, "Just buck up your sprits", "Pull yourself out of it" or "Think about something positive" don't help. When you are a state of depression it is difficult or impossible to do these things - it's a function of the condition. And pressuring or goading in an attempt to get someone to "Snap out of it" is normally counterproductive. Instead, learn to be a good listener and ask soft questions that give the loved one a chance to explain what they are feeling and going through. Listen openly with interest, but avoid getting deeply drawn in to any negative stories.

Speak to the real person, not to the behaviour or pattern of depression. Remember that they are not this pattern, they are the being who is experiencing it. Speak to the wisdom in them, expecting a wise response and you might just get wise answers. Brandon says, "Speak to the Buddha nature and you are likely to get the wisdom of a Buddha in reply."

Quick fixes rarely work. Suggestions of some activity, exercise or distraction might seem like an antidote to depression and, though they can sometimes bring a temporary lift in mood, their effect will at best be short lived.

Encourage diagnosis. If you suspect that someone close to you is suffering from depression encourage them to see a medical practitioner and get professionally diagnosed. This is often a major first step to admitting the problem and doing something about it.

If your friend or relative is taking traditional medication for depression, no matter what your opinions about such drugs are, support them positively to follow through with the medical advice they are receiving and the medications they are taking. You should never encourage anyone to stop taking professionally prescribed medication. When they are ready to explore stopping any such medications, that process should be closely administered and monitored by a qualified medical professional.

Remember that you can't fix or heal anyone. Pushing or insisting that someone does something you think will be good for them can often be counterproductive. It can cause resistance, stubbornness, or it can encourage a resentful, dogged participation that rarely produces positive results. An important rule of any personal transformation is that the individual absolutely must make their own decision to try a new technique, or undergo a specific treatment. With Journeywork no particular belief is required, but the genuine willingness to give it a go is a must.

If your loved one is willing to try Journeywork then you could help them by recommending that either they come to a Journey workshop where a variety of people will be diving in deeply and clearing their own life issues; or you could point them to one of the thousands of amazing Journey Accredited Practitioners who practice in many countries around the world. Details of both approaches can be found on our web site www.kevinbillett.org/book-bonus

Mostly, be patient, with your loved one and yourself. Depression can be tiring and frustrating to be around, so give yourself plenty of breaks and make sure you follow some or most of the healthy living guidelines outlined above. Your own mood can be deeply influenced by the company you keep, so make sure to seek positive and outward looking company, so you also get the support you need.

And above remember that thousands of people from different cultures and traditions around the world - people who have been through severe traumas, people whose lives have been turned upside-down by unexpected losses, bereavements, illnesses and anxieties - have freed themselves completely and for good by using the Journey techniques laid out in this book. The work is based on simple, solid and well-proven principles, and is always worth a try.

Use Journeywork Regularly

Brandon and I have been immensely privileged to have access to this healing work for more than two decades. It is genuinely the most potently transformational work that we are aware of on this planet, and we choose to regularly use it to stay healthy and clear, to make sure we are living life as a reflection of our true potential as human beings, and to make sure that we are open to life living fully through us, with the prayer that it uses us in highest and deepest service to its own purpose.

We recognize that over the years we have both absorbed, been conditioned by, numerous negativities and traumas. We have made it a part of our life purpose to continue to open inwards, to continue to surrender, clear out the crud. We continue to let go of the past and forgive ourselves and others for old pains. We have decided, in honor and reverence to our deepest self, that we will continue to clean and polish our inner diamond for as long as there is breath in our bodies.

So we highly and strongly recommend that you do something similar. Using Journeywork as a matter of habit - maybe once a week to start with, then once a month or so - will not only transform your life, it will keep you on a path of openness, of self-love, of truth. You could simply find a friend with a similar prayer - maybe by sharing this book with them - and ask them to cross-process with you on a regular basis. You can revisit the audio recordings of the processes and keep clearing out those old issues. It can only get better!

Or, if your prayer for freedom is strong, you could decide to come to a live Journey event, such as the Out of the Blue workshop or The Journey Intensive. Trained and skilled helpers will support you as you undergo the work and you will be able to complete at a deeper level, and learn some of the more advanced Journey skills to further enhance your understanding and ability to use the work. Of course, we are able to share many more insights and healing techniques, and more comprehensive Journey Process work in these workshops than we could include in this book, and we can offer more hands-on support to help you through any specific challenges you may be experiencing.

We have an in-depth curriculum that includes a Journey Practitioner Program, which is an absolute jet-plane-in-freedom experience. It is a five-module course that is so powerful that it is capable of transforming and liberating each and every aspect of your life. It is a personal/spiritual growth fast track that will blast you into a life beyond your ability to dream it.

Please take a look at the many options and available courses, workshops and life transforming retreats on our web site: <u>www.kevinbillett.org/book-bonus</u>

And in the meantime, whether we meet in person or in consciousness here as a result of your reading this book, our prayer for you is the same. May the universe flourish you; may it find, expose and use every talent, every genius, and every particle of your being in service to the totality of all life. May the love deep inside you burn so strongly that it burns through everything unlike itself, and leave you knowing yourself as pure, boundless love. And may you enjoy, revel in, and be fulfilled and nourished at the deepest level by every moment of this momentous ride called life!

Kevin & Brandon

Recommended Further Reading

Brain Chemistry and Drugs Myths
- The Emperor's New Drugs: Exploding the Antidepressant Myth - Irving Kirsch
- Depression Delusion Volume 1: The Myth of the Brain Chemical Imbalance - Dr. Terry Lynch

Cellular Healing & Personal Transformation
- The Journey - Brandon Bays
- The Journey for Kids - Brandon Bays
- Living The Journey - Brandon Bays
- The Biology of Belief - Bruce Lipton
- Molecules of Emotion - Candace Pert

Emotions and Decision Making
- The Decisive Moment - Jonah Lehrer
- Descartes' Error - Antonio Damasio
- Emotional Intelligence - Daniel Goleman

Spiritual Freedom
- Freedom Is - Brandon Bays
- The Diamond in Your Pocket - Gangaji

Articles
- Depression: It's Not Your Serotonin - Kelly Brogan MD. GreenMed Info January 4, 2015. www.greenmedinfo.com
- New study throws into question long-held belief about depression -ACS News Service Weekly PressPac: August 27, 2014. www.acs.org
- Depression is NOT a chemical imbalance in your brain. Here's Proof. Dr. Joseph Mercola. April 6, 2011. www.articles.mercola.com
- Why antidepressants don't work for so many. Northwestern University. EurekaAlert! October 23, 2009. www.eurekaalert.org
- The biggest cause of anxiety and depression is traumatic life events. (Depression is not a disease.) Dr. Joseph Mercola. November 19, 2015. www.articles.mercola.com
- Is a happy life different from a meaningful one? - Jason Marsh & Jill Suttie. Berkeley University California. www.greatergood.berkeley.edu

Gratitude

Our huge gratitude goes out to all the people who support The Journey worldwide, friends and colleagues alike, and special thanks must be mentioned for a number of especially wonderful and big-hearted people.

To Gaby Burt and Cliff Burt, our deep love, respect and gratitude for your precious friendship and for partnering us in The Journey with such devotion, love, openness and surrender for twenty years. It is a privilege to dance the dance of life with you as friends, and we love and appreciate you both more than we have ability to express.

To my sister, Debra Billett, big love and gratitude for your openness, willingness, love, and your exposure, dedication and support for The Journey over all the years. And thank you for being my sister!

Deep, everlasting thanks to my closest friend, Kevin Thompson. We laughed and played through the best of times, and you supported me with love and care through the worst. You have always been my 'sanity, reason and hell, yeah, let's do it anyway' mentor. Long may we continue to travel, surf and philosophize together!

To great friend Neil Padfield, thank you for the big-hearted personal and practical support that takes so much frustration out of our lives and allows us to focus on The Journey and projects such as this one. And eternal thanks for booking that first Journey session. It truly was a life changer!

To Michal Andrejco, our huge thanks for dedicating your life to this work and partnering us in bringing The Journey up to modern technological speed. And to Daniel Wagner, heartfelt gratitude for coming on board with us so completely, so quickly, and bringing conscious effectiveness to our organization's marketing. And massive thanks for your love, expertise and help in shaping this book.

Huge thanks to our dear bestie, Vicki St. George, for many years of deep and supportive friendship and for being the editor and advisor who elegantly shaped and refined the early drafts of this book.

Loving thanks also to our close friends Lisa Kossowsky and Yosi Kossowsky. Lisa, you brought patience, expertise and a lot of love to streamlining this final draft, and Yosi your suggestions and refinements were great enhancements. Thank you both!

Our deepest love and gratitude go out to all the extraordinary Journey Staff, Presenters, Partners and Accredited Practitioners worldwide who dedicate their lives to serving humanity in this way. We cannot name you all here, because the list would run on and on... and please know that your openness, willingness and huge-hearted surrender to awakening and healing always blow us away. Your presence, authenticity and support in this joint venture in consciousness brings delight to our hearts and big smiles to our faces whenever, wherever we meet, and when we read of your participation in life's awakening and healing 'miracles'.

Deepest, most profound gratitude to our beloved spiritual teachers, H W L Poonja (Papaji) and Ramana Maharshi, the embodiment of freedom, who invited us to stop and directly, ruthlessly enquire into the nature of the Self. We bow in awe and love of the infinite awareness your presence forever unveils and reveals. We pray that this same truth resonates in and emanates from every word in this book.

And our ultimate gratitude is to life itself, to the animating force, the awareness, the infinite love that is the true nature, the essence of all being.

Namasté.

Selected Feedback for Kevin's Work:

"This is an extraordinary way to unlock the grip of depression. The work is so deep and accessible and provides an exquisite vehicle to your soul. Your heart longs to sing its song and this seminar unlocks the words. Simply fabulous!"

- Nicky

"Great processes - went deep, really pulled the rug from the withdrawal - really pulled it and out went the suffering and in came freedom. My mind still doesn't believe it and that is okay cause my body has a direct experience of the truth of it and my mind will catch up. Amazing!"

- Donna

"The workshop will open you to deep freedom, the essence of yourself. It will take the veil and dissolve the black cloud of depression that prevented you from seeing the beauty of life."

- Dominika

"I came to this event thinking I could probably experience just a little 'lightness' because I don't actually suffer from depression, but the whole weekend blew me away. I realised that I don't need a label of clinical depression to benefit from clearing blocks that stop me feeling good about myself and life. I feel like a big shift has happened in me and am feeling very positive about all that is about to come."

- Petra

"Fantastic weekend which helped me unblock and release so much. To access deeply buried emotions and release them was beyond therapeutic. To realise I have a choice regarding depression is very enlightening and to be able to access and know my own answers is amazing."

- Emma

"Out of the Blue blasts out of the water the myths, labels and lies about depression. I highly recommend this experiential training to all those suffering under the cloud of depression and those that are simply not living the life they'd love."

- Kathryn

"There were times when I felt like I was in solitary confinement with depression. I resigned myself to living the rest of my life in a kind of maximum security prison. When I came to Out of the Blue I hoped it would transform that into at least an open prison - I did not expect this work to offer me the key to the door of freedom! Thank you Kevin."

-Laura P.

"The best news ever! Out of the Blue cured my post-natal depression in a day. Your book will help so many people. Drug companies, beware!"

- Ilana K.

"I have lived an entire lifetime under the erroneous belief that depression was a genetic inevitability, an inescapable inheritance, one for which I would invariably see transmitted to my children. Through various tools of healing and yoga, I managed to largely overcome depression, yet without vigilant adherence to these tools, it still hovered there, threatingly ready to reveal itself and reinstate its territoriality into my life.

After doing the workshop with Kevin Billett, I managed to identify the roots of this unwanted legacy, and rip it out from the very core. The workshop helps to distinguish the myths from empirical fact, and gives accessible and effective tools to deal with patterns of depression both personally as well as for use as a Journey practitioner with clients.

Kevin is an impeccable teacher, highly astute, as well as wholly accessible for questions and clarification. He has the rare gift of being to able to transmit both factual and esoteric truth, is deeply intuitive and exudes in both his teaching and his comportment, the channeling of grace itself. The workshop evoked for me, a profound healing and catalyzed a deeper state of awareness and stillness. Indeed I journeyed right out of the blue and into the peace that is my own essential nature.

- Nicki F.

To find out more about Kevin's 'Out Of The Blue' workshops and to find qualified Journey Practitioners, go to www.kevinbillett.org

Made in the USA
Columbia, SC
19 November 2018